MY VILJANDI

JUSTIN PETRONE

My Viljandi

ESTONIAN
SMALL-TOWN BLUES

PETRONE PRINT

Special thanks to Estonian Cultural Capital

Editor: Epp Petrone
Copy editor: Penelope Piip
Layout: Heiko Unt, Aive Maasalu
Map illustration: Kudrun Vungi
Maquette: Madis Kats

ISBN 978-9916-605-75-2 (print)
ISBN 978-9916-605-76-9 (epub)
ISBN 978-9916-605-77-6 (epub)

PETRONE PRINT

www.petroneprint.ee

Viljandi näib olevat ajast maas, aga ta hoiab oma väärtustest paremini kinni kui Tallinn ja kuldne ring selle ümber.

Viljandi looks as if it is stuck in time, but it has held onto its values better than Tallinn and the Golden Ring around it.
(Historian Heiki Raudla)

CONTENTS

MY QUARANTINE SPRING

The day before they closed the borders, there were whispers in the cafe that the government would do such a thing.

I believe it was Heldi who told me first, over breakfast and cappuccino, and Jõeste was also there. Heldi with her button nose and dolled up looks, and Jõeste with her chocolate hair and dangling earrings. Usually, we talked of such trivial things at breakfast. Frivolous vacant things. But life had turned serious. The era of coffee talk was over.

It was because of the terrible sickness, they said, the dreadful virus that had been spreading throughout the lands, and cases were popping up closer by in Saaremaa and Võrumaa. It seemed that all you needed was one sneezing Estonian freshly arrived from Milan and within weeks you would see peak occupancy in the hospitals, rationing of ventilators, and death.

Still, the closing of the borders had a special, end-of-days, apocalyptic 1930s flavor to it. It felt as if we were about to pass through another moment of no return. When I was a child, I already sensed the difference in older people, even children of that crisis. I tried to imagine what life was like during the Great Depression, or even the Second World War, but couldn't. For Estonians, the war was real and they tasted its blood in their own mouths, but for Americans like my grandparents, they heard the stories via radio broadcasts or in newspaper headlines, or in watching neighbors be informed that their son would not be coming home from the European theater. All that was just unimaginable to me. Yet now, just a few days into quarantine, it has become much more imaginable. Now, I can imagine almost anything. In just a few days, just a span of hours, borders can close, realities can alter, people can die. All it takes is a few days.

And now, from today, the borders are closed. But local souls are undeterred. My industrious neighbor Kristina is still out in the yard sanding wood in her coat and work boots. Who knows when she will again see her Italian boyfriend Alessandro. As for me, I venture out into this eerie world, driving to the forests of Viljandimaa to avoid people. I've been back to the Crow Hills, and to Põrgu, the cave down in Loodi Nature Park. Most of the shops are closed here. The sellers at the apothecary wear masks. The famous Viljandi landmark Green House Cafe is still open, and you can get a good macchiato *tume röst* over there. The baristas keep the required distance. Yesterday, I bought a cup from there – with mask and gloves on – and strolled around alone. I wondered when or how I would see my American family again. Or, even go elsewhere in Estonia. But somehow, I just couldn't leave Viljandi. The town wouldn't let me leave.

The weather was brilliant and the sunlight did justice to the crumbling ruined houses. There is something very worn, very ancient and frayed about Viljandi's Old Town, something that brings to mind the villages of the French countryside with their rickety fences, chipped facades, and sprawling gardens. This is an enchanted place. It's like a fragrant, haunted chateau. It invites romance and decadence. There is no town like it in this country, or in this part of the world.

Down by the lake, I watched from a distance as a young woman with golden hair reclined on the docks and enjoyed the sun. I watched this lake woman for some time, how she sat in the light and crossed her legs. The water shimmered and the reflection of the trees lining the lake danced about. There was not another soul around. Just the two of us, the air and the water. Then I thought of this book, and how I had finished it just weeks before, in some other reality. It's already a bygone era now, and I was grateful I had written it all down, as it had happened. These were my reminisces then, my memories of life before the crisis. Already it seemed like a long time ago when I had returned to Viljandi on a southbound train one evening. But it had had been only a few years ago.

Just a few years! It seemed like an eternity.

Viljandi, Estonia
Spring 2020

THREE AND A HALF YEARS EARLIER

"Deep autumn had set in, with a crackling wind from the west."
(F. Scott Fitzgerald (1896–1940), "The Crack-Up", 1945.)

I come into Viljandi on a southbound train, a smooth straight ride through the forests, the wind crackling at the windows. The land here is level, the forests a delicious mix of deciduous and pine – these trees being among the lushest, most satisfying personalities of this northern land. Trees are supposed to inspire hope and sanctuary, lust and love. Yet the bodies on the train this afternoon are weary, limp, resigned – the people's eyes glazed over like the first autumn frosts.

It's September, dark mornings, dark evenings, the winter solstice looms ahead.

The Viljandiers on the train are already tired of it, and yet enjoy the lull, the chill, the crackling wind at the windows, the autumn hush. Thick masses of dough-white flesh, straw hair, angled features. A pink-gold sunset glows through the trees. The lullaby rattle of the train. I tug out a notebook and start to write the scene.

Here I am, a New Yorker bound for Viljandi. Imagine that! I used to have a long list of reasons for being on this southbound train. I used to have a long list of reasons for being in this country. I was married to one of its people. As far as they were concerned, I had become one of the tribe. Yet now those reasons have been blown away, like the wind scatters the leaves across the forests. My marriage is over. I suppose I'm homeless in the very deep sense of this word.

More wind against the windows. The next stop is Sürgavere. A few old ladies disembark.

For the longest time, I had wondered what I would do if my marriage ended. There were various escapist fantasies – a mountain somewhere in the Pacific Northwest, a fishing village in Greece. What I kept coming back to, after the smoke from the dynamite had cleared, was that I would find a place to settle down and devote myself to writing, which seemed to be the only thing I was any good at anymore. The solitary writer's life. There was a saintly inevitability to it. The point of no return. I imagined myself rising early, getting my coffee, and going to work. I had never devoted myself to anything before. I had been too cynical and too unsure of myself for that in those days. Yet if there ever was a time for a clean break, then the moment had arrived for my transformation. And this small town, Viljandi, seemed like a place that could support this lifestyle. It had once been my home years ago. It could be my new home again.

The disembarkation at the station, all of the vehicles speeding away into the dust, and that deep evening haze already descending. The welcoming committee is the jazz singer

Hedvig, who shows up in a plaid shirt and rubber boots (*kummikud*) and drives me into town. She has allowed me to use her apartment while she returns to her countryside retreat in Tuhalaane village.

"*Tere, härra kirjanik!*"

A very warm embrace. When she hugs me, I feel not only that I am being welcomed into Viljandi, but into a new existence all together. Her plaid shirt. Those rubber boots. Hedvig has reddish brown locks of hair and her face is covered with freckles cut by two slanty eyes. She laughs like a pirate and, I have to admit, I think she's insane, even by my lax standards. Every other sentence has some innuendo or double entendre. "*Sisse, välja!*" she winks as we pull onto the road that leads into town. "In and out! *Out and in!*" She pauses a moment to admire the sunset – "Oh, what colors over there!" – and then we are off, with some jazz song on the radio.

There are instructions about the apartment, which are basically that I will have the run of the place, "*aga muidugi teisi naisi siia ei too.*" "But you won't bring other women up here." It's agreed. There's no one to bring. We arrive at the house on a nice old-fashioned boulevard, and park around back. Up a staircase into the apartment. It's a fine place with tiles on the kitchen walls and a lacey bedspread. In the backroom, children's toys are spread quietly across some tables.

Then, with another great hug, the singer's off again, down the streets in her jeep. Her furnaces in Tuhalaane require attention. The wood goes in, the heat comes out. "*Sisse, välja, Justin! Välja, sisse!*" That naughty peculiar laugh of hers again. That cackle. I keep thinking this is all just a film, that my life will eventually go back to whatever was normal before, after the film ends. But this is too realistic to be a film. Hedvig is real, I suppose. I stare out the window after she's gone. Look at the orchard, the clothesline. I run my fingers on the table. This is my new reality awakening. All right here.

I leave my bag at the foot of the bed, tuck my notebook into my pocket, and head out.

I'm not far into town when I'm overcome by the cyclists. They swarm down the main street, part of some local bicycling event, and have the run of the place, old men, young ladies, children, on all types of two-wheeled contraptions. They really look like some kind of lost, uncontacted tribe.

There's a kind of sloppy bohemian-ness to the Viljandiers, an essence of being that is only half-preserved in some derelict wooden ghetto neighborhoods elsewhere in the country, like Karlova in Tartu, or Kalamaja in Tallinn. But unlike in those places, the people here all seem to know me. They call out to me as they flutter by in reflective wear like a school of fluorescent fish. I've almost forgotten that I once belonged to the town, years ago. Our small family belonged to this town. I remember how I used to go to the *Huvikool*, the Hobby School, and tried to fetch my two older daughters from some art class, and how frustrated I was with them as they tumbled down the stairs laughing, like in some old comedy film, and would play tricks on me as I pulled the sled, and both hop off at the same time, sending me lunging forward into a snowy embankment. I remember the haunting words of the marriage counselor from that time. "You and your wife are not normal people. The chances of you having normal children are less than zero."

But they are not here anymore. It's just me now. A local boy, the teenager Mano, comes riding at me on a bike with his fist raised in the air in a sign of Viljandier solidarity.

"Welcome back, Petrone," the young man yells. "We always knew you'd come back!"

I write this all down in Cafe Fellin later, enveloped in its interior of Dutch tiles and tinkling wine glasses. Sweet cakes shine from behind the glass at the bar. Smooth young couples sit with wine and plates between them making the delicate chit-chat of love. Light jazz plays on. There's a smell as clean as dripping candle wax. I'm alone, watching the couples gaze into each other's eyes. But I was always kind of alone, wasn't I? I've been alone for ages. I've been sitting in a basement sauna in Tartu waiting for my wife to come back from wherever. India? Australia? Who knows where she went. And sometimes I went and wandered around too, alone. It doesn't matter anymore. Now, my lonesomeness is merely official. The English writer Aldous Huxley never ate here, but his words ring true all across Cafe Fellin tonight. "In all circumstances we are by ourselves." It's a Huxley kind of night for me in Viljandi. Maybe I do need some wine?

Here comes the owner Merit with a big glass full.

This is a woman whose clothes move with her, a flowing, full-piece knit dress that ends just above the knees. She has the best kind of personality, someone who relishes your attention and then gives, lovingly. Without any dialogue, the undercurrents of the room shift around her. Most of us are like little boats making little waves, you see, but this woman has the energy of an ocean liner. She is also quite pretty. A lioness's face. I tell her and her husband, Mr. Aivar, who sits across from her, that they look so young.

It's good to flatter the hosts.

Mr. Aivar is clean shaven, has a mop of dark hair, and I notice the silver watch resting on his wrist, near the cuff of his sleeve. Tonight, it catches the light from the many candles. Aivar is too well dressed for Viljandi, I think. To be a proper Viljandier, one needs a jacket that's at least 20 years old and covered in blood and straw, plus stained pants and a bagpipe. His jacket looks new and his red pants might as well be Versace. The fact that he looks like an outsider makes me trust him more.

Merit owns Fellin. She is a Viljandi cafe oligarch. When she decides something, it happens. Many stories begin just like that, "Merit decided that ..." I am drawn to her power. Like most men, the absence of a feminine counterbalance in my life has knocked me off course. I am now a ship without a sail, without a port, with an unruly, mutinous crew. I am a lost Greek sailor.

Merit has decided to leave tomorrow for Crete. A village near Agios Nikolaos in the east.

"*Agios, agios, agios,*" I say.

She stares me down as if I really am a ghost.

"This is the Greek word for 'holy,'" I go on. "They say it in all their ceremonies. I know because I spent some time in a Greek Orthodox monastery."

There is silence and candlelight. Then the Lioness makes an announcement. "You have changed."

It strikes like the chime of a clock.

"What do you mean?"

"You seem more like you."

"I do?"

"You are more like yourself than you were before. More honest."

"Well, I have to be honest. There is no other way forward for me anymore."

Merit lifts a finger. "Your Estonian is better, too."

"Eerik, eat your fries," Aivar instructs a small, yellow-haired boy who sizes me up from across the table. Even as a toddler, their son has the stoicism of a full-grown Estonian man. He eyes me with suspicion. There is something unfamiliar about this man seated here before him, his dark hair, his dramatic expressions. He's untrustworthy. A foreigner.

"*Ära karda,*" I tell the boy, who furrows his brow. "Don't be afraid. I'm totally harmless."

Eerik grimaces and covers his face to cut me out of sight.

"He's in a phase where he's afraid of strangers," shrugs Aivar.

"So," Merit places a soft hand on mine. "How is it?"

Aivar looks up from his food and Eerik is still glaring.

"How is what?"

Merit just waits. How is it? I know what she asked.

"It's like death, I guess," I say at last.

No member of their family moves. They are waiting and I continue.

"I really feel like I have died, and yet somehow I am still stuck in this body, with these arms and legs, and this name. They say that this is who I am. People remember me but I don't."

Merit pauses. Then she pats my hand a few times.

"It's like a new start. Sometimes you have to end it all, to get rid of it all, all of the memories, all of the traumas. You have to end the past, let it all go, and give yourself time to heal. Aivar and I did it too," she looks across the table at him, "and two years later our love was even greater than it had ever been. You just need to give it time and see where it takes you."

"Yes, but ..."

"Did you decide to do it?" Merit asks. She has a soft, intimate voice. We were always fast friends, the two of us, since the day I met her at the Green House Cafe years ago. She had a dream to build her own café that long-ago day when we met. And here she is, in the middle of her own kingdom, or queendom. I can see all the couples chattering behind her, telling each other sweet things, dreaming of unending love, of being soul mates. One day each one of the couples here might marry. Then more than half will divorce. Yet some of their dreams will come true.

"It's complicated," I answer.

"Of course, it is!"

"I know it's a sad story. We don't need to talk about it."

"No," Merit raises a finger. "It is not a sad story. It's your story. It's one chapter from your life. That's all it is. Now you must begin a new chapter."

I pause and see that Eerik has now crawled over Aivar's lap to be by my side.

"See," says Aivar. "He's not afraid of you anymore. Say hello to Uncle Justin."

Eerik pats me on the cheek but still eyes me with caution, as if I might be a bit dangerous. I'm not, but I'm full of emotions.

"Do you want to finish my wine?" Merit asks.

"Yes, please."

Blood-purple red. Sweet, dry, and tangy. This is glass number one, but there will be more.

The walk back to the apartment is desperate and satisfying. Viljandi's Old Town has a psychedelic tinge. All of these bright cartoon houses, like a child's misplaced toys. The Old Water Tower. The Grand Hotel. The pawn shop and abandoned *striptiis*. Lights go on and off in people's windows. Black cars sputter over cobblestones.

On the way, I pass under the windows on a side street. We once lived a comfortable life in this very house, the five of us. There was a father, a mother, and three lovely girls. Our youngest child was born right in there behind the window glass. I slept in there each night, and took my children to school in the mornings. I would go to the cafe and try to work. I was just as much a part of Viljandi back then as the statue of the painter Johann Köler in the park.

Then it all ended.

I turn up the street and follow it all the way down. I look at the ivy on the buildings, the fruit on the apple trees, the crooked wooden barns. It's early autumn, but the smoke is already curling up from the chimneys, and this time I enjoy the musty, rich smell of it. I used to hate furnaces and chimneys when I used to live here. I came to hate everything when I lived here. I was embittered, but by what exactly? I can no longer say. Perhaps by having done too much too young? Back at Hedvig's place, I reach the house, climb the steps and enter the apartment. I unlock the door, undress and climb into bed, pulling the blanket over me.

Sleep does not come at first. Instead, I study the halos the street lamps cast across the ceiling. There is a cat in the apartment, my only companion. A fluffy female tabby. She sits on a chair in the corner, like a sphinx, licking her paws, observing the night with those slits of eyes.

I look to her for comfort, but she yawns through the dark and licks herself.

Tomorrow, I will see her.

THE DESIGNER

"Viljandi, my beloved Viljandi. I went to Tartu yesterday and there were so many cars! But now I am back here in Viljandi and just look at her, how pretty!"
(A young woman overheard on Posti Street.)

The Designer lives in a small flat on Mäe Street overlooking the Orthodox church. In the evenings, you can see her bent over her sewing machine through the window. The lamps in the apartment emit an orange glow, and she keeps a mannequin beside her desk upon which she drapes her experiments.

She isn't content with the way the shirt hangs this time, but if she works on it anymore, the project will go to waste. So, she makes a big pot of tea instead. She pours herself a cup, stirs in some honey, and walks over to admire her view of a broken, forlorn street. She has chunky locks of gold-colored hair. This flaming bush is sometimes visible through the window from the street. Because of this, she is known often as, "the girl with the hair."

The Designer irons her dresses and irons them again. She watches documentaries about minimalism and makes another pot of tea. Her suitcases are packed away beneath her small bed. They are full of textiles she has picked up along the way in Reykjavik, Berlin, London, Stockholm, and other places. She really cannot help herself, but she keeps getting more.

The Designer came to sit with me in the summer during the Viljandi Folk Music Festival. I had known her for years, but we had never really talked. It had always felt though that one day we would talk, and whenever I would see her, the memory of her would linger. Most would dismiss it as a mild crush. There was more to it than that. It wasn't just that I felt that I would know her for a long time. It was that I understood that I had already known her for a long time. Her almost clockwork arrival to my side the very week the divorce had been announced was therefore utterly predictable. Everything I had once feared, everything I had once dreamed, it was all coming true. This was all part of the upside-down dream I was now living. I couldn't tell her that though. If I did, she might think I was crazy. Maybe I was a lunatic? After our first encounter though, we continued our dialogue, and I came to visit her too. Something new started to fill me. I lay on her floor and then poured out my heart to her, about my real-life troubles.

She listened to my stories and thought it over. The Designer has very wise eyes.

"What you most need now," she said, "is total silence."

It was mostly because of her that I started coming back to Viljandi that fall. I would come in from Tartu and we would meet at the cafe and go for walks down to the lake, or to the Castle Ruins. We would sit under the clouds on the pier, or in the grass and breathe in silence. We had plenty to talk about back then. I trusted her completely. Such strength, such poise. All I wanted was to have someone set me straight. To point me in some direction. For this, I would pledge all my love, all the devotion I had. I would worship her the way the Hindus worshipped Gayatri. I would walk around shrines. That was the deal, as far as I saw it. I was in. But she wasn't. She told me as much. We could meet sometimes, she said, but only just meet.

I wasn't listening.

And once, a leaf fluttered down from an old oak tree, and I caught it in my hat.

So, I started to believe that I had found a new true love, a new muse who would help me give birth to a new writerly life. A life where we lived as twinned artists on the hillsides of Viljandi, she with her sewing machine, me with my journals. She was exactly what I needed, I thought, a sturdy, secure woman. A woman on the same continent. Just a few months out of the bleak end, I had somehow stumbled into a pretty new beginning. It was almost too easy. I drove around Lake Võrtsjärv, eyed the clear blue water stretching to the horizon, and felt a stirring in my chest. Then I saw the slanting roofs of the old Viljandi villas again. I parked my car on Koidu Street, took a seat outside the Green House Cafe, greeted my old friend Mr. Aivar as he stepped from its green wooden doors with a hot cappuccino to go, steaming up in his hands. When he inquired why I was back in Viljandi, I told him the truth.

"I've come to see the Designer again."

When the lucky girl at last arrived, I was thumbing Scott Fitzgerald's debut novel *This Side of Paradise*. I loved that book and Fitzgerald. I loved the stories of sledding parties in 1913, of old-fashioned courting rituals and all the sad young men. The idea began to grow in me, of becoming a dedicated writer. All I needed was a new home.

All I needed was her.

"And can you imagine, some people don't even want to write well," I blabbered to her over coffee. "They just go to school and get regular jobs, find good-looking mates, take some nice vacations. They never want to write well, or do anything extraordinary. They're just happy. Imagine that!"

The Designer listened carefully and then she spoke. She had ordered her Americano and cinnamon bun as usual and was picking at it and picking at it. Her expression was flat, taciturn, but she did look quite beautiful as she spoke, and I noticed the gold in her hair again.

"You have no right to complain about your life then," she said. "You have chosen this life for yourself. All of these things that have happened to you. You have brought it all on yourself."

"Is it really that bad?"

"You are divorced and you have no money. Could it get any worse?"

My new love has her own troubles though, both global and local. She dreams, and she worries, then tells me that she's not worrying. She wants to be a "superwoman," in her own words, to birth an environmentally sustainable fashion brand into existence. Viljandi has gifted her with a support system, a community of like-minded artists, a tapestry of colorful memories.

("This town that has always meant so much to me," says this girl about her Viljandi. "Just look at it. It's like a big outdoor spa!"). She says Viljandi is a place where people come to regroup, reorient, recuperate. They come here to get their lives together before they move on. Some never leave. They stay and stay. She could live in London – where she worked as a waitress, or in Reykjavik – where she worked in a design shop, or even in Tallinn, but she chooses to be here now. She is, by unanimous consent, seen as *töökas* (industrious) and *tubli* (accomplished) and always has been. Her work hangs on the walls of the local Academy. She is a Viljandi queen.

Yet she needs stability and just wants to stay, but then there is the question of money. How does one bring a brand to market? She is destitute. She lives off vegetables from her grandparents' farm. When she goes to the shop, she buys one tomato. She frets, but says she is not fretting. Sometimes she curls up in her room and cries, but no one sees her cry. To me, she is like Estonian nature itself, those landscapes that seem breathtaking and punishing at the same time.

The Designer got her black gloves at Sõbralt Sõbrale ("From Friend to Friend"), the popular second-hand store on Kauba Street. She imagines them on the handlebars of a Vespa in Italy someday. Viljandi is for now, but a brighter future awaits. "Can't you just see me in Rome?" she says.

I try to think of ways to help her but this is no good. It threatens her independent spirit. Even Designers ascribe to the do-it-yourself ethic here in Estonia. She sent me a photo of her father and the car he built made out of parts that he got at the store. This is the mentality of the *maarahvas*, or the country people. "Thanks for your help," she says, "but I can manage on my own just fine." "Fine" is another of her words. She may be struggling, she may be on the edge of watching a lifetime of dreams crumple up in a slow-burning blaze, yet all will be "just fine."

"What's the worst that could happen?" she asked once at the cafe.

"It might not work out."

"Then I will have to figure something else out. You'll see. Everything will be just fine."

I hoped it would be. But most of all I hoped she would love me back.

INSIDE THE WHALE

"The personal lives of these Viljandi people add up to something out of a soap opera. Sometimes when a baby squints at me in the supermarket, I wonder if he thinks I might be his father."
(A British photographer who has spent several years in Viljandi.)

I love her. There is no question about that, though I don't want to love anyone. There is a bit of a war going on. The classic, eternal struggle between heart and head. The heart wants to love, you see. It wants to sing, and it yearns to write. But the head says, "No, no, no! The last time you followed your heart, you wound up in a world of pain. The heart is a catastrophe just waiting to happen. For the head, 'love' just won't do. Even as I dream of the Designer on lonely nights, even as this euphoric longing for her overcomes my body, my head keeps it all at arm's length. Love is just a trick, it says, like some flimsy Christmas decorations that aren't made to last. It's all just another feeling, and feelings are like sauna *leili* steam. They come up hot and fast, make you ache all over and then they are gone – to where, no one knows, or can say.

I enjoy it though, because it's something new, something to take my mind off of things. There are more visits back to Viljandi, and sometimes the Designer comes and walks with me by the lake while her boyfriend stays at home making sauerkraut soup (*hapukapsasupp*).

She agrees to meet me a day or two before my birthday. We have dinner at Fellin. It's candlelit, and she talks of her search for employment and of her creative endeavors. I imagine her in her apartment, with its crates of textiles and baskets of yarn, piles of books, and that ceramic mug with a little coffee and almond milk still in it. At the center, is the sewing machine. That's the heart, the sun around which everything orbits. Spanish music clicks on in the background. She wants to go to Spain, she says, maybe to live someday, if she doesn't make it to Rome.

The sewing machine has an old motor and whirs as she runs its needle through a length of fabric. Those times I had been there before, listening to the whir, I felt a peace I hadn't known in years. I closed my eyes. I haven't been back in the nexus of her apartment for a while though.

There is another man there. One who makes her soup.

"There is a friend of mine I would like you to meet," the Designer announces casually over dinner on my birthday. "I think you two will have much in common. You're so very similar."

I chew slowly. I look into her eyes over the candlelight. I look at them for a long time until I get some sense of what is going on. There is something behind them, but what is it? For a moment, I see a softness in them and then the eyes harden again. What is it? Something is going on. *The friend*. It has to be a trick. Love is always a trick or a scheme. I am being set up.

After dinner, we walk to Mulks, the cavernous bar on Posti Street. The friend is sitting at a table in a loose, eastern-looking shirt. She has chocolate hair, beautiful lips, and special eyes. I want her at first sight. Something thunders inside me. She looks like some misplaced Yupik girl. I look at her dreamily first and then she tells me to go to hell. Then I tell her to go to hell. "You're full of shit," I tell her. "*Ei, sina oled ise sittaga täis*," she clamors back. "You're full of shit yourself." Our contempt is mutual. This much I know. The whir of the sewing machine in the heart, overtaken by the cacophonous laughter of the friend. The reaction to her is visceral, grotesque, but it thrills me. A new life force is flowing through me now. The Designer sits in the corner watching it all unfold. More glasses of wine are ordered, the conversation becomes more unsettled, sinister. I can see myself with this wild friend of hers. The Designer cringes deeper into the corner as we order even more wine. I can see it. I will marry the friend, and soon after she will smash dishes on the floor. Then she will threaten to kill me and we'll make love.

Maybe we really will die but it will be a beautiful, messy death.

It's an unruly aspect of myself I have hidden all this time with the Designer, trying to be taciturn, to be *tuim*, trying to be a Viljandier, for whom love should be gossamer thin, for whom life is views of a shimmering lake and crisp folk music. The Designer does have a romantic side to her, I take it, a sort of kissing in the rain in the London parks in a soaked dress, 19th century romantic side, buried and hidden away from me, but that is a long way from my Viljandi now. Each bottle of wine undoes a button. I'm just not a Viljandier. I'm a lost Greek sailor. My blood boils hot like red sauce. The madman is loose. The autumn wind crackles beyond the door.

"I'm leaving," the Designer announces suddenly to our table and rises. She places a gloved hand on my shoulder. I'll never forget the feel of that glove, that impersonal, almost clinical feel it has. "Good night to you," she bids to me in a dry way, "and also to you, my friend," she says to her companion. Then, with a toss of a shawl about her neck, she walks away.

"See," the friend says, shaking her head. "This is what she does. She leaves!"

"But where are you going?" I ask. "You can't just leave us here like this."

"Goodnight to you both," she says again. The glass door closes behind her. There is a rare quiet inside. It's as if she took all the oxygen in the room away in the room away in her coat pockets.

"Well, what do we do now?" I say to the friend. "Just go home?"

"Not a chance," she snaps. "You're coming with me to the lake."

Down to the lake. She feels my neck with her hands. "God, you are so tense. Do you feel that? *Pinges (Tension)*! You are so horribly tense. What happened to you?"

"Are you a masseuse or something?"

"Yes, actually."

"Ouch!"

"Unbelievably tense. You need to loosen up!"

"Shouldn't you go back to her place?"

"What do you want with her anyway?"

"I just think we should go back to her place."

"You have something for her, don't you?"

"Not at all."

"Just say it then."

"Say what?"

"Say it now. Right now, right here, on the spot."

"Say what?"

"The truth, you fool! Out with it!"

"What truth?"

"Just say it now!"

"Fine then. I love her."

"Was that so hard?" she clicks her tongue. "Why is it always so hard?"

"I'm sorry."

"It's okay. She knows. She loves you too."

"She knows? She does?"

"But not like the way you love her," the friend shook her head. "More like a pet mouse, or a rat."

"A pet rat?"

It's as if I have been pushed off the Empire State Building. If she had said pet rabbit, or pet cat, I would have understood. The Designer treats her cat like a prince. But a rat? This lower, ugly life form? The world tumbles beneath me. The girl feels it. There has been a rupture. All the pressure that has been building that autumn, and the years beyond it, are now being released.

"I want to go home now!"

"Just come with me," she says. "You shouldn't be alone tonight."

Two shadowy figures weave through the labyrinth of the town. All of those rickety fences, winding lanes, feral cats, crumbling buildings with the wind howling through the rotting window frames. Viljandi is like some kind of Estonian *favela*. From outside, it looks innocent, even quaint. When you are in it though, you become enveloped, engulfed by it. You breathe Viljandi in, and it swallows you whole, down into the belly of the whale. The whale dives, deep into midnight. You wind up walking to the lake in the dark with some mysterious woman.

On a frozen beach, on a frozen swing, we sit together, my heart still in freefall (*"Like a rat!"*). Our breath rises up like ghosts. The steam from our warm bodies. I melt into her like sugar. The lights on the hill from the old villas. Once again, I am at the mercy of womanhood. Jonah had been swallowed by a whale, but I feel as if I'm being swallowed by a whale's vagina.

"I'm sure you love her," she says, "But you actually need to love yourself before you can really love someone." We are so warm together, as warm as the inside of an Inuk snow house.

"You really think I don't love myself?"

"This is obvious."

"How can I love myself then?"

"That's something you have to do on your own. I'm still trying. If you really loved yourself though, treated yourself with the respect and compassion that you would for someone you loved, then you would have women like this." She flashes her fingers in front of my eyes. "Ten times ten times ten times ten. You'd have to fight them off to keep them all away."

"I'm not sure I need so many women."

"You can even choose! Don't you see? This is exactly why you love her. Because she loves herself. She respects herself no matter what. She is independent and that's what pulls you. Do you think you're unique? You think you're alone? Every other man loves her for this."

"But I'm different! I just wanted to bring her *hapukapsasupp* when she's sick!"

"She already has someone who brings her *hapukapsasupp*."

"I'm sure he's a fine man."

"He is, yes. Very fine."

I looked up at the villas on the hill and shivered. All those glass windows. How many people were up there watching this debauch now? Maybe everyone. Mayor Ando Kiviberg would no doubt soon walk by. "Tere, Justin! And who is this fine lady with you in the snow?"

"What was your name anyway?" I ask the girl. She sits with her back to me, staring at the icy lake. She said she wanted to go swimming but I told her it might not be such a good idea.

"My name?" For the first time she seems flustered and looks around the beach as if she can't be bothered to even remember it. "You actually want to know my name?"

"Please tell me your name."

"Cloud," she whispers. "My name is Cloud."

I leave Miss Cloud at a deserted playground and walk back to Hedvig's Old Town apartment alone through the cold. The neighbor's cat is in the stairwell eyeing me again. I lean down, scratch it behind the ears a few times, and then enter the apartment, only to see the very innocent-looking bed there and get in. Again, I feel as if I am dreaming. All of Viljandi is a dream. Maybe I am just dozing somewhere on a beach, back in New York. Sooner or later, I will awake. These are my thoughts as I crawl into the bed. It takes until the morning light for the full effect of the alcohol to wear off. I'm afraid Miss Cloud will never wear off.

To think, I had once met a young Estonian woman just like this in Helsinki years ago. Back then, I was ready to follow her to the end of the Earth. In a way, I did. Am I really ready to do it all over again?

Coming down Koidu Street the next morning, I walk directly to the Green House Cafe. It's 9 AM, the bells are chiming all over town, and the beautiful sun is up, turning the facades of the old buildings into crisp, cornered silhouettes. Enn is already at the door, waiting for me, smiling in his thick winter coat, those joyous jumping eyes, the wisps of his gray hair dancing in the wind. He's the proprietor, but this morning he might as well be sweet Jesus on the Hill of Golgatha.

"Hey dude, what's happening? How are you feeling this morning?"

How am I feeling? Clobbered. Ravaged. My pretty small-town romance was just assassinated by an Italian madman and some girl who looks like a Sami witch who calls herself Cloud. In a few hours, I have known love and despair, heartache and compassion, clarity and drunkenness, the whir of the sewing machine and the glaze of a frozen playground. Pushed off the Empire State Building, swallowed up by a whale. In the Biblical story, the whale took Jonah to the ancient Assyrian city of Ninevah and vomited him onto the beach. That's how I feel.

"When I was a kid in the Eighties, my brother used to throw these wild parties, Enn. These were crazy, anything goes. Remember that Lionel Richie song, 'Dancing on the Ceiling?'"

"Of course! *'Oh, what a feeling!'*" He sings the first line.

"I think people were actually dancing on the ceiling."

"Sounds like fun."

"I feel like I just got back from one of those parties."

Enn just grins and puts a hand on my shoulder. "Fantastic! That means you're doing good! You're living the life! Man, I had the best time in the Eighties. We had a great time. The very best time. It was a riot! C'est la vie!" He kisses the air with his fingers, in a dramatic, French kind of way. "Hey, come in. I'll make you the strongest macchiato I can muster. On the house!"

DREAMING ABOUT FIRE

"Then he knew what was wrong. He had forgotten to build a fire and warm himself."
(*Jack London (1876–1916), "To Build a Fire", 1902.*)

I have in my possession a tin of Indian Instant Coffee I purchased from the Konsum on Koidu Street. A hundred grams of brown powder. The text on the tin is written in characters that look like Hindi, and there's an image of a girl dancing. I turn it over in my shaking hands. This *Product of India* is now the sole warmth-giving thing in this apartment, the Chef's place. After a year or more of living in limbo, I've moved from Tartu to Viljandi to try it out as a writer's retreat. Here I am.

This is it, the great leap forward.

I had actually sworn off Viljandi after the Drunken Birthday with Miss Cloud Incident. The Designer cut me off completely after that. She will barely speak to me after I blamed her for setting up the fraught meltdown of an evening. "No, no," she said. "I had nothing to do with it."

And yet I still came back to this town. I came back, as I said, to write. Who needed these women anyway? The only things they were capable of dishing up were heartbreak, lies, and misunderstandings. At least I have my friend the Chef to support me. He knows what it's all like.

"Ha! Women? Who needs them! Nothing but trouble. Come and stay at my place," he had told me. "Stay as long as you like! I won't be back from Australia until the end of the month."

"Are you sure?"

"Of course! You are my brother and I am your brother. We are brothers."

It was a nice brotherly gesture, but he forgot to leave me the key to the wood barn, which means the whole apartment is like a frosty ice box. It's January now, minus 20 degrees, the wood barn is locked up tight, and the toilet is frozen. You press the button and all you hear is a sad dry click. The room stinks of icy piss. I am pacing around trying to stay warm and find a solution.

I boil the water in a small kettle, gray wings of steam rising into the air of the dim kitchen. Glance outside the window. Fluffy sheets of never-ending white cascading down. Even with three blankets I can't stay warm tonight. It's a two-room tiny place, with two furnaces. Most houses in the Old Town still have wood heating, you know. According to old timers, Viljandi didn't even have indoor plumbing until the 1960s. Central heating is still a luxury in the Old Town. It's a city of smoking chimneys, the smell of burned wood, a place that feels primitive.

The furnace here in the kitchen heats the main room, the larger one in the back heats the bedroom. However, the place has been cold for weeks, and a deep frost has set in from the east. There's no wood and the Chef left the barn keys with his yoga instructor. I got in using the spare key under the front door mat. There is a shower and toilet in the corridor. These are both frozen.

It's 4 AM and each time I pull the blankets on top of me, I toss about restlessly because the cold finds a way in, nips at the end of my nose, or a bare foot slides out and is exposed to the chill. The kettle reaches a boil, and I deposit spoonfuls of the Indian powder into a ceramic cup, fill it with water, and add cream. A musty, satisfying taste. I take a seat at the table where a sketch pad and pen sit idle. So much for the writer's life. I gulp the coffee and boil another pot.

Enough hot water will thaw the toilet.

The only solution I can think of is to trek through the blizzard to Statoil to buy some of the firewood that comes in bags. Two bags should heat the place until I get the key to the barn. I dump another pot of hot water into the toilet and press the push button. Still nothing. Then I suit up in my jacket and boots and head off into the snow, down Koidu Street all the way until I reach Jakobsoni, crossing through the parking lots to the tantalizing blue glow of Statoil at 4:30 AM.

I buy two bags of overpriced wood and lug them across town to the little apartment, crouch before the larger furnace, stack the wood, and get the fire started, watching the flames. I hold my hands to the fire, but the room is cold, and even the roar of a fire can't banish the frost.

My heart is so heavy, my face feels cool and rubbery. All this work, just to stay warm.

Miss Cloud is now the only woman who will still speak to me, and only in two-week intervals. Exactly two weeks. It's like she's out on the sea somewhere, and then once in a while her radio signal becomes clear. *Do you read me, Miss Cloud? Do you come in?* The rumor was that she had returned to her parents' farm in Virumaa where she slept in the sauna beside a big hairy dog. Just the thought of Miss Cloud can summon her spirit. It's almost supernatural. There is a softness in her that I crave. Cloud is always soft with me. I need that softness. I ache for it. If her softness was chocolate, I would eat myself clean through to the opposite side of Earth. That is how hungry I am for her. And suddenly the phone buzzes. "*Mis teed?*" she texts. "What's up?"

"I'm freezing to death in Viljandi."

"Oh. Then get closer to the fire."

I sit by the furnace, push my socks to the fire. Steam starts to come out of the cloth.

"It's not working," I say.

"Well, you need to get closer then."

"Is this some kind of ancient Finno-Ugric wisdom?"

"Passed from generation to generation. My great grand-mother told me in the sauna."

"I'm still cold though."

"Then you're not close enough."

"But I'm very, very close, Miss Cloud."

"You should just get closer."

"I wish I was closer to you."

"Funny."

"Is it warm up there?"

"It's always warm here."

"I think it's too far for me to come though. I don't even have a car."

"Just get closer to the fire, *Härra* Petrone."

"If I get any closer, I am going to be in the fire."

"One can always get closer to the fire."

"Then I will try to get closer."

"*Tubli*," she says and vanishes.

I fill the furnace to the brim with wood, stuff it in deep, and make a makeshift bed beside the fire and pull the blankets over. Again, I will sleep alone in Viljandi. My body feels good beside the fire though and I run my fingers up along my torso and down my legs. I feel soft and smooth beneath the blankets and I think of Miss Cloud. Then I sleep and dream. I dream of fires.

Later, after another pot of hot water, the toilet starts to work. Civilization returns to Viljandi.

I have a Christmas gift for the Designer that I have been carrying around in my bag with me all this time, just in case I run into her because, as noted, she doesn't care to converse with me after the Drunken Birthday with Miss Cloud Incident.

When we do meet, by chance at the cafe, she softens her stance, and invites me to her flat with its beautiful sewing machine and music (this time Frank Sinatra). We drink tea at her table. Her boyfriend is gone somewhere.

"But I am your friend," she says. "Always your friend. This has always been clear."

"I know that."

"Do you really?"

"I just thought you had tricked me. That you set me up. To get rid of me."

"No, never," she looks away. "I would never do ... that. That would be unfriendly."

I eye her over the table. I know there is something else she wants to say, but she just won't say it. There is some mystery here. She is very good though. Very good at secrets.

"I need to go somewhere now," I say. "People seem to think I'm moving back here to Viljandi. Everybody in town is talking. Apparently, I am already moving back but don't know it."

"But you are moving back," she shrugs. "This has been obvious for some time."

"I am?"

She nods quickly. That seems to settle it.

"I have something for you," I say. I reach into my bag and pull a small rectangular package from it. It's covered in holiday wrapping paper. I push it across the table, and she undoes the wrapping. The gift reveals itself to her, as a paperback journal I had found in a bookshop in Stockholm over Christmas. The cover is an illustration of a woman with long curly red hair.

"It reminded me of you. I didn't want to buy it, but I felt compelled to."

The Designer frowns. "But I don't have red hair."

"They didn't have a journal with your exact hair color."

"It's fine," she says, setting it aside. "Thank you. I needed a new design journal."

Then she shows me the door. Once again, I'm out in the cold.

NO OTHER CHOICE

"Sometimes you just have to leave. You don't want to, it breaks your heart to, but you have no other choice but to leave and start over again."
(Enn, a seasoned spirit, chatting over morning coffee.)

It's probably that night that I inform my children's mother that I will not be returning to our shared house in Tartu. It's long overdue, us separating, but it's made me wretchedly sad. I have this drawing of us all together that my youngest daughter had done at the preschool. There is so much love and fun in that drawing. I keep it on the shelf in the Chef's bedroom, my makeshift bedroom. I stare a long time at the picture, and then I go and make myself an instant Indian coffee again.

Yet a day or two later, comes word that Anna, my second eldest, wants to come and live with me. We pack all of our possessions into the back of the Volkswagen and move to Viljandi. There is a special meeting at the Waldorf School and it is decided that she will be accepted. Even in the sadness of leaving Tartu, there is the hope of something new here. That night, we eat together at the Nepalese restaurant on the corner of Tartu and Lossi Streets, trading stories with the men from Kathmandu who always shake their heads "no" when they mean "yes." It's a melancholic, yet very hopeful time, and the sight of the town in the snow comforts us both.

This girl, still just nine years old, with long light hair, dreams on the couch, as I sleep in the backroom, my clothes still in bags. After school, her old Viljandi friends come and visit. They gather around her, eyeing her curiously as if she has washed up from a shipwreck. In a way, we are shipwrecked, and I have come to think of our new house as if it was once a capsized ship, like that boat house that the Peggotty family lived in in Charles Dickens' book *David Copperfield*. In the book, the old fisherman Peggotty lived in a converted boat-house right on the coast of the sea. Whenever I see the planks of wood on the street side of our house, I think of Peggotty's place.

There is an apartment next door to the Chef's that is being renovated. Kristina, a jovial, rosy cheeked local designer about my age, who can be seen at night hunched over her sewing machine, repairing dresses and fixing trousers for many needy customers, is also busy renovating it. I tell her I want the place at once, and she promises to have it ready in a few weeks. During the evenings she and a local builder named Urmas work on the apartment, which has a restored, red-tiled wood furnace at its center, clay-spackled walls, and smooth wooden floors.

I feel quite good in the new house, and even though we look at other places I know we will stay. There is an old house in Kantreküla with a bathtub that is still heated by a stove, and a smaller house beside the Orthodox church with an even more ancient and complicated heating system. A little bit down the street, there is another fine place for rent, but its main setback is the smell coming from the neighbor's apartment. This is because the neighbor – an older fellow with a white beard who looks like a sea captain – doesn't have a toilet in his apartment.

The real estate agent informs me that the old man uses a bucket.

But that is life in the Old Town. Rough-edged and ragged, yet ever intriguing.

We wait patiently for Kristina to finish the apartment, which is fine, because the Chef isn't due back for weeks. Until, he shows up out of the blue, as he has a habit of doing.

Yet, such is the nature of the Chef. He's just full of surprises.

THE CHEF

"An ounce of sauce covers a multitude of sins."
(Anthony Bourdain (1956–2018), "Kitchen Confident-
ial", 2000.)

Who is this man, the Chef? For me, he's like a wayward younger brother, and for him, I am no doubt the same. Both foreigners, both in Viljandi, both divorced. It's hard to tell which of us is more of a disaster. He is at least Swedish though, which means he is, in a remote way, of this place. His people ruled this land for 150 or so years. It was these imperial wars against Polish-Lithuanians and Russians that eventually brought down most of the walls of the Viljandi Castle. It's hard to imagine our Chef in royal uniform fighting off Russians though. I imagine his ancestor was a scallywag with messy hair and a pencil-thin mustache making soup in the rearguard.

But, even when he's just making soup, he gets into trouble.

For example, the following story:

I was seated in the cafe of the *Spordihoone* (Sports building) which is across the road from Fellin, and enjoying a cappuccino after dropping my daughter off at volleyball practice. As soon as my phone rang, I could sense that something was wrong. The Chef only calls when there is some kind of issue. That, or he's made salmon soup and needs someone to eat it. This time it was trouble though, not the soup.

"The police have been chasing me since Paide. You have to help!"

"What do you want me to do?"

"How about you take my car into town and I can drive yours?" I could hear his heavy breathing, and sense his heart pounding over the phone.

"You want me to drive a car that the police are looking for?"

"Yes, exactly."

"And you want to borrow mine so that they don't catch you?"

"Sure, why not?"

"I'm not sure that's a good idea."

"Well, you've got to come and get me then. You just have to come now! Get out here now! I just saw another police car go by. They're after me! I'll leave my car on the side of the road, come back, and get it tonight. Maybe I can even get someone else to come and get it."

I agreed.

"This is just crazy," the Chef said minutes later, getting in my car. He had two duffel bags with him and wore a scarf around his neck. His hair was greasy and messy and he had grown a faint mustache during his time in Australia. Although it was getting darker, he still wore his sunglasses. There is a touch of the '90s rock star to our friend the Chef, as if he used to play drums for Oasis.

"I saw them point at me in Paide," he told me in the car. "Then I turned down a dirt road to get away. So, I pulled behind an old barn and hid out there for a while. Waited and waited. Then I saw the police car go shooting past, with its sirens on, all blue and white, flashing. Then another just zoomed past! I got this feeling in my chest like my heart was going to explode."

A serious look, he motioned to his chest. He said he took the backroads all the way to Viljandi. It took him hours. He refused to enter town though on account of having to pass the police station. As he talked to me, I saw another police car race down the road. Then a long-haul truck stopped. The officer got out and walked to the door of the truck and banged on the door.

"I know they've radioed for me," said the Chef, sinking down in the car seat. Word is out across the country. 'Be on the lookout for a renegade Swede.'"

The winter sun was setting, casting shadows on a purple horizon of barns and trees as we drove into town. The place looked somber and tired. Viljandi seemed like the kind of town where if the police caught you, they might just give you a pat on the back and buy you a cup of coffee.

"I'm sure you will be fine," I said. "They've probably given up searching."

"If the police catch me, I'm done with Estonia," the Chef said.

"Ah, this is how you do it. See?" The Chef shakes the eggs in a jar and pours them into the pan. Then he folds the omelet and removes it before it's cooked through. "That way it cooks on your plate, but isn't overdone. Hey, these are organic eggs. You want some? You'll have to pay me."

This is his old house, his house of memories. With his ex-wife away, his former mother-in-law watching the children, and me utterly dependent on his generosity, he's permitted me to stay here in the old place, sleep, and feed the cat, but for how long? The apartment still isn't finished. Soon we'll have to move to a rental house on Kauba Street, and if it's not done after that, there are apartments for rent at the Ingrian House around the corner. Sooner or later, we'll get into the new place, but again that shipwrecked feeling. We live out of boxes. My life as I once knew it is now over. For the Chef, who also recently split from his wife, it's the same story. In every sense we are in the same boat. Cut loose. Adrift. Abandoned. Shipwrecked. There's a kind of terror in these circumstances, but a thrill too. The thrill of learning to trust yourself again.

"We're put out on the street, like empty boxes," the Chef jests. "Take him. He's free!"

I cannot help but laugh. There is something so charming about such an epic failure in life. Years ago, we were role models maybe. We were fathers, husbands. Now we're something else. Divorced men. It sounds kind of dangerous. Yet we still have hearts and souls. We still have stomachs. He grates cheese into the eggs, sprinkles some herbs he's been saving since spring, the ones he collected down by the lake. Then the water boils and he's ready to make the coffee. This is his ritual, for the Chef is a Swede and this Swede only drinks Arvid Nordquist, the highest quality of Swedish brands. Moreover, the Chef is particularly drawn to blends that are only available on the Swedish markets. The Estonians only have a few blends on sale. Yet the Chef always manages to bring in the contraband blends from Sweden. So, he's not just a speeder. He's also a coffee smuggler!

And once, in the north of Sweden, he allegedly robbed an ice cream truck. In his defense, the door was unlocked.

"My favorite blend is Amigas, the one picked by women," he guzzles away. "So smooth."

I can't help but like my friend the Chef. I like how shameless he is. If he wants the ice cream, he takes the ice cream. If he wants the coffee, he takes the coffee. He gets divorced and he's already got an active Tinder account. I'm in love with two girls who are best friends. If the police come, he hides out behind a barn and then takes the backroads into town. There is a bit of swashbuckling rogue to this man. Maybe he really is descended from some royal cook from the time of the Great Northern War. Everyone else was busy blowing up Viljandi, but he was in the back with the big cauldron of fish soup whispering to himself, "The Chef never gets killed."

"I wonder what the police would have done to you if they caught you?"

"Oh, they probably would have locked me up. I was evading arrest."

The fire roars, the air smells of bacon and omelet. From the window, the lake is a distant gray abyss. Every now and then while forking the bacon out of the pan, the Chef pauses to watch a car turn up the street, then breathes a sigh of relief when he sees that it's not the police.

"Trouble, trouble," he says and touches his chest again. "I'm in so much trouble."

The Chef believes the Estonian police are about as human as Arnold Schwarzenegger's character in *Terminator*. He's sure they have an image of him from their car cameras that they have matched to an internal database.

They're coming for the Chef. It's only a matter of time.

"Maybe they would have given you the police brutality treatment," I say. "Except Estonian style." I lift a piece of firewood to demonstrate. "Maybe one of them had a trunk full of birch firewood," I raise it up into the air and let it swing down. "On your knees, you damn foreigner!" I act out the police's assault on the Swede. "Take that, you goddamn Swede!"

"Not even funny. By the way, do you need more cream? I bought it today. Fresh."

I accept his offer and tip back my cup. This is our thing. *Fika*. It's the word for the traditional Swedish coffee break. Married, unmarried, we return to the sacred ceremony of *fika*. Another hot coffee. A bit of fresh cream. Maybe the Chef is right. Maybe we don't need women. "The genders," he proclaims, "should be entirely separated! Of course, we can meet for sex now and then, but I am fed up with their nonsense."

I'm not quite ready to give up my dream of women just yet, but I nod along.

"Too bad we don't have any chocolate. Then it would be a proper *fika*."

"But we do," I say, unwrapping a chunk of Kalev that's been in my pocket.

"Oh, man," he breaks off a hunk and lets it melt in his mouth with the drink. "This is just what I needed." He looks out the window. Another car has passed, but the police haven't arrived.

"Are you still done with Estonia?" I ask.

The Chef stares into his coffee and then looks up. "You know Australia was great, man. When I saw those kangaroos hopping along, I cried. I really did. I was crying."

"Why don't you go back to the kangaroos?"

"Viljandi just seems like an interesting place to be. You're here and so is the Designer." He looks up and smiles. "So, I'm staying."

"That's a relief. If you'd left me here, then I'm not even sure why I'd have moved."

"True, true. But that also means you need to find your own apartment."

"I already have. It's right next door to yours. They are finishing it as we speak."

"But that means we can have *fika* every day!"

"Yes. But let's not overdo it."

I peek out the window at the houses that line these hills. In these houses have lived writers, poets, painters, and musicians. I think that Viljandi has always been a refuge for people like us, castaways, chefs running from the police. Some houses are vacant, a few have collapsed. Across the street, the Designer's window is dark. The bell of the Orthodox church next door clangs. It's Sunday. Up and down the streets go, until they arrive at the pines and the lake. The church bells echo. Smoke curls from the chimneys, and then all is as quiet as a patch of country.

SIMON THE ENGINEER

""Mulks", the popular wine bar on Posti Street, welcomes donations of wooden chairs. The chairs have to be in good condition. Every person who gifts a chair gets a free bottle of wine."
(Margus Haav, "Sakala" newspaper, 2017.)

In Viljandi, gossip is as thick as February snow. Where better to get it than at Mulks Bar on Posti Street? It always has ten or six local alcoholics in it. Half a dozen wooden tables, pathetic little candles. (And somehow inspiring too – how they keep on flickering.) Drunken laughter. Stinks like a bar too. I don't love Mulks – or any bar for that matter – but it's a great place to write, a great place for stories. I usually drink one of the stronger Italian wines. Only one or two glasses though. Three and it's a mess. Four and it's an incident. Five and it's *kompromat.*

Outside there is snow and silence. Deserted streets that stretch off into white and black. Yes, I know this isn't the top of the world, but it might as well be. I open the door and go in.

I've actually come to Mulks to meet with Simon. He's newish to Viljandi. He needs my assistance. An English sound engineer and musician with a wonderful mane of shoulder-length black hair who's always dressed in black, he has the best, most eternal of English faces, like one of Charles II's distressed cavaliers from the English Civil War. Simon the Engineer would look perfect with a ruffled collar, a cutlass hanging off one of his hips. Our Simon drinks lots of tea when he is not busy with sound equipment, or his keys, or dreaming of going on tour again. Some whisper that he is a bit posh though he assures me that he has relatives that are even richer.

At Mulks, he plays "Girls on Film" by Duran Duran on the speakers. Simon loves Mulks and comes in every chance he gets. For Christmas, his lady even bought him a Mulks gift certificate.

He arrived in the most peculiar of ways, as a backing musician for the group Modern Talking during RetroFest a few years back. He was only supposed to come to Viljandi for one day. But that night he met a local girl and, soon after, twin daughters were born. Now he teaches sound design at the Academy. He's never really left, you see, though he insists that he does not live in Viljandi, but is merely visiting. We shall see, Simon. We shall see.

Tonight is Simon's night out. On most mornings, he can be seen pushing the wide pram down Viljandi's mottled, icy streets. In it sleeps his twin girls, brand new Viljandiers of English and Estonian extraction. In the evenings, the little Anglo-Estonian girls are with their mother and Simon is here with his black hair, his wine, and his Duran Duran. Viljandi. It's the Bermuda Triangle of lost foreign men.

"What you need is a crash course in Estonian-ness," I inform Simon the Engineer on this Saturday night at Mulks. "It's time for you to set aside your defensiveness. Time to get you on a program."

"Go on."

"Lesson number one. Start stacking wood. Learn how to build a good fire."

"This is a disaster. Do you know how much time goes into wood heating?"

"I do."

"It's a huge amount of time out of your day."

"Look, I used to be just like you, Simon. You must accept it. No going back."

"Bollocks!"

"The time has come for you to also embrace the sauna. That's lesson number two."

"Never. I'm never going to do it, mate."

This is interesting, as Simon has a sauna in his apartment. He lets his friends use it.

"Why not?"

"It's gay."

"You don't like squeezing into a hot room with a bunch of naked men?"

"Gay."

"All up close together?"

"Gay."

"Packed in tight?"

"I'm not going to the sauna with you, mate."

Thus ends my attempt to Estonianize Simon tonight, this Saturday night at Mulks. There is a bit of a lull. Then enters Simon's big Finnish friend, Heikki.

I'm not sure if Finns count as full foreigners in Estonia. They know the terrain better, understand its idiosyncrasies. Finns – at least the ones I know – never complain about the weather or about wood heating here. Heikki is a Finn in Estonia. He moves among the locals as if he was at a family outing with relatives. Finnish Heikki looks normal enough. He's a big man with a thick white beard and graying hair, a woodsman's shirt, thick arms. He has his own bottle of wine and pours me a glass. He pours Simon one and we sit with him. Heikki starts to speak in a deep voice.

"I have a bit of a situation," he says.

We rest our elbows on the table and gaze at our big Finnish friend.

"I have a local girlfriend. I have a woman in Finland with whom I have some children. She's coming to Viljandi. For the first time, my Estonian girl and my Finnish girl will meet."

"You have two girls?" I ask.

"Yes. The thing is, I told my Finnish woman, 'Okay, you can come and visit, but you should know there is another woman with me. Viljandi is a small place. No matter what you do, the two of you will meet.'"

"You told your Finnish lady that you have another lady?"

"Oh yes," Heikki says. "She knows I have another woman."

"She's not jealous?"

"She said it's okay if they meet. She's coming."

"You really have two women?" asks Jack.

"I've had more. I think the most I have had at the same time is four."

I slurp down the rest of my glass and Heikki pours me another. *Four?* How does a man who looks like Santa Claus have four women? And I have always been devoted to one? I throw myself at Designers, and Cloud Women, and nothing sticks to me. And yet he's got *four*? Clearly, I have been doing something wrong. Time to take some notes. Time to study up on Heikki's methodology.

"So, ahem. If you don't mind me asking, how did you even manage that?"

"Simple. First you have one woman. This is woman number one. When woman number two comes along you say, 'I have a woman. She is my number one woman. You can never be my number one woman, but if you like, I will let you be my number two woman.' If she agrees, you have two."

"What happens when number three comes along?" asks Simon.

"Simple. You have two women. Number three comes along. You tell her, 'I have a number one woman. You can never, ever be my number one woman. I also have a number two woman. You can be my number three woman. If you try, one day you may become my number two woman. But never my number one woman. Are we agreed?'"

"She agreed to that?"

"Yes, she agreed. It's not really a problem until number four comes along. When number four comes along you do it again. Do you want more wine?"

Simon and I both nod yes, and Heikki refills our glasses. For a big man, he is remarkably dexterous with the wine bottle. Each glass is poured precisely.

"*Kippis*," I say and Heikki returns the toast with his glass.

Simon stares. I'm not sure if he knows what it means.

"Okay, you boys wanted to know about the fourth woman, so I'll tell you. So you have three women The fourth one comes along. You tell her. 'I have a first woman. You can never ever be the first woman. Never in your life will this happen, no matter how hard you try. I have a second woman and a third woman. I don't think you can be my second woman, either, but, if you try to please me, then one day, if you are lucky, you might, just might be my third woman.'"

I gulp down the second glass of wine.

"See, it's not so hard," says Heikki, who tips back his glass. "You just have to be clear."

"You should write a book about it," says Simon.

"But I am!" Heikki says and smiles. "It will be in Chinese and cost 50 cents."

"Why Chinese?"

"China is the biggest market. There are 1.4 billion people, 700 million of them are men. That's 700 million men who could benefit from using my tried and true methods. Plus, it's cheap to print in China, so we can charge only 50 cents. It's not an expensive country, but it adds up."

An image of villages full of Chinese men leaning up against their bicycles, gathering around to digest Big Finnish Heikki's new tome on *The Art of Having Many Women* appears in my mind. Like the delicate stroke of an archaeologist's brush, it seems to uncover some ancient aspect of the male psyche, one that at times these days plays havoc with me. The pressure to find someone. Find someone, find someone. Find anyone, anyone. Find someone now. "You know what you really need," a dozen people both male and female have advised. "Another woman."

At the door, the Designer appears like a ghost with snow on her scarf. She takes a table at the front, and slips into a card game with two other ladies and only barely glances my way. My heart sinks a bit and I ask Heikki for another glass of wine.

Find someone. Find anyone. Find someone. It motivated Heikki to organize himself a life with four women when maybe he needed none. This is all in the lost male handbook it seems.

The one that Big Finnish Heikki is writing in Chinese.

WHY ARE YOU IN VILJANDI?

"Do you know where we are?"
(Viivi Luik (1946–), "The Seventh Spring of Peace",
1985.)

After many such nights, I inevitably return to the back kitchen of the Green House Cafe in the mornings, where Enn serves coffee before the cafe opens its door officially at 9 AM. Here he gets the early morning local caffeine junky set, who stumble in, hair all wild, jowls heavy drooping, crusty dead eyes, ghost faced, pasty pallor, like French aristocrats on their way to the Guillotine. Slumping humanity without coffee. Four heavy sacks of potatoes. That's us.

One is me, another is Maaker the guitarist. Then there are Jõeste and the cool-looking man in the broad-brimmed hat that everyone calls "Köler" because he looks like the statue of Johann Köler, the famous painter, in the park. His real name is something usual, normal, and forgettable. And so, to us he is just Köler and he waits for his coffee just like the rest of us.

Enn is made of something else, something not fully human. I look at the eyes beneath the cap, the nose, whiskers, ruddy skin, like it was stitched together from the belly of an alligator.

Who is this guy?

Six kids – wait, no, eight total – he mans the machine in that back kitchen behind the cafe, banging on the espresso maker's filter, that wonderful and reassuring metallic clanging sound that lets every coffee thirsty molecule in your blood know that, yes, it will be soon.

Joan Baez's beautiful canary voice is on his playlist, cooing elegantly of "Joe Hill," because there's always a Manhattan coffeehouse in Enn, wherever Enn may be.

Born in a displaced persons' camp in Germany in August 1945. Raised in New Jersey. Drafted to Vietnam. A foggy interlude in Puerto Rico. In local parlance, he's a *väliseestlane*, a 'foreign Estonian', still Estonian, but *võõras*, strange, unknown. He calls me "dude". For Enn, it's still 1964, and Joan Baez and Bob Dylan are new folk singers and they're still together.

There are four plastic buckets of beans on the counter, either for sorting or roasting. What a stash! Beans from Colombia, Nepal, Mexico, *Honduras?* All here in Viljandi. It's like a travel agency, the cafe, each coffee is a ticket out. When I pull up a stool, I plunge my sleepy head into the bins, just to get that aroma of sunshine up the nostrils. The Colombian smells the best to me, rich, but that's me. The Nepalese smells like coffee, but still, it is Nepalese coffee, which means that it's almost Tibetan coffee. Sounds kind of holy. His Holiness the Dalai Lama's enlightened coffee.

"Hey, dude, what's happening these days? What can I get you?"

"Macchiato dark roast. *Tume röst.*"

"All right, dude. Coming right up!"

He clangs away and the machine grinds and steams. What a delicious sound. From these beans, great things. I'm the first one in, but before I know it the rest of the team assembles, Maaker, Köler, then at last our lovely Jõeste. Every day is the same here in Viljandi, same actions, the weather changes, but the circuitry keeps us buzzing along our magnetic trajectories. You see the same people on the same street corners, get asked the same questions, such as:

"But why are you in Viljandi?"

This is what Jõeste asks me after she staggers to her stool between Maaker and Köler. Enn begins to run the orders for them. Maaker stands – he is so eager for the coffee that he can't contain himself – and Köler looks up bemused from under his amazing hat, but only just barely.

Jõeste is our woman and prefers to be. I once called her a person, an *inimene*, by mistake. She scolded me, "But I am not just an *inimene*, Justin. I'm a *naine*, a woman." Dark masses of chocolate hair, blue eyes, a fine profile, Jõeste's presence is subdued but comforting. Of all of us, she is the most alert, and yet I can still sense her body's hunger for that caffeinated infusion. Her morning skin, deadened by March gloom, has not yet attained its most vivid midday glow.

She wears a red scarf draped around her head, one with a stylish, vaguely Oriental pattern. She got it from Pskov, she says. This is how they look, the best teachers at the Viljandi Culture Academy. They are like models, always on display even at 8 AM in search of coffee.

I should tell you something else about Jõeste.

She's not from Viljandi.

Jõeste is from Rapla and Enn is from that displaced persons camp in Germany. Maaker, the guitar player who can't sit down, who has a handlebar mustache and suspenders and looks like an extra from a French avant-garde film? He isn't from here either. He's from Kuressaare in Saaremaa. What about Köler? The old cowboy with shoulder-length hair, who can turn any question into a meandering philosophical elegy? ["But what is a person's profession, really? I've never had a profession! Even in preschool when they asked me what I wanted to be when I grew up. My profession has always been being myself!"]

Köler is from Tallinn! Nobody in Viljandi is actually from Viljandi. We wound up here by accident. Simon the Engineer came for one concert, and you know what happened next. I came in January to write in the Chef's apartment and now I'm renting the place next door. It's March and I still haven't left. I may *never* leave. So Jõeste's question, "Why are you in Viljandi?" is rather important. Her excuse is the Academy. "I'm still teaching at the Academy," she says when I ask her.

What's mine?

"What do you mean exactly?" I stall for time and sip. My macchiato tastes like a cookie. They should just hook me up to Enn's machine and run the stuff straight through me forever. That's why I am here.

"It's just not common that a foreigner would move to Viljandi," Jõeste says.

Enn slides a drink before her and she relishes its aroma.

"Is there a certain reason you moved?" Jõeste squints now, all detective-like, her eyes more alive. "Do you have a *silmarõõm*?"

What's a *silmarõõm*?

To translate: *silm* is 'eye' and *rõõm* is 'joy'. Therefore "a joy to the eyes". A woman? Jõeste wants to know if I moved here for a woman. But, my dear Jõeste, even if I did move here for a woman, even if I did, do you really think I would announce it to a back room full of Viljandiers on a rainy March morning? I've been in town long enough to know that talking about your emotions can get you into trouble. People will spread them as news, or even try to analyze your mind state. Soon all the grannies in Uueveski Street will know about your *silmarõõm*, and the party planner will organize a wedding reception with pork and *kringel* and violins, while Razumova the real estate agent in the long black coat will have stalked you up a deal on an old house with restored wood-heated furnaces. "These will keep you warm even when it's minus 25 degrees!" She'll say.

Such are the terrors of the truth in Viljandi. One must learn to divert, to distract. One must practice the sacred craft of shutting up, of being quiet. *Suu kinni!* It's easier that way.

"Viljandi is my *silmarõõm*," I answer. "It's just so pretty."

Jõeste sips her drink, squints at me, and says nothing. She knows everything anyway. People here know more about me than I do. They read it in today's *Sakala*. It's all written.

"Heh," snorts Maaker the guitarist, his eyes darting. "Viljandi isn't anybody's *silmarõõm*."

I had always thought that Maaker was *normaalne*, an average *kütt* or dude. The more time I spend with him though, the more I suspect he may be a touch strange. After he grew his wily handlebar mustache, I told him of similar plans to grow my own thick and fuzzy horseshoe, one of those downward facing growths that bring to mind a stoic and manly Ukrainian Cossack. Maaker just dismissed me. "That kind of mustache only makes people depressed because it faces down. My kind of mustache curls up at the end, see," he toyed with its waxy ends. "It lifts the spirits," he moved both arms in an upward motion. "My kind of mustache makes people happy."

Unfortunately, Maaker can only see his uplifting facial hair in the mirror. Without his coffee, he's more subdued, almost morbid. He stands waiting. Enn is still clanging away and Joan Baez is still singing. *"How many roads must a man walk down, before we can call him a man?"*

"If Viljandi isn't anyone's *silmarōōm*, what is it then?" I ask.

Maaker's coffee at last arrives and he stares at it. His eyes are moist. He hands Enn his card, and Enn autographs one of the boxes where there should be a stamp. If you buy eight coffees, you get one free.

"Hasn't anyone here told you yet?" says Maaker. "Viljandi is the last stop in life." (*Viimane peatus elus.*)

A muffled chuckle and then a titanic sigh as the truth sinks in. There's heavy rain now outside, big gray wet sheets of it making that staticky impenetrable noise. Sometimes I do feel like we are hiding out beneath a waterfall in this mossy, half-rotten place.

It's about time I admit to myself and to anyone who cares that it is true, that no man can live without a *silmarōōm*, or rather a woman in his heart. I can't. The heart is hungry, starved for it. Yet even when the heart gets one in trouble, Viljandi relieves the stress of it. The days grow longer. The Old Town is splashed with the paint of sunlight and the ice on the lake cracks apart into mirror-like plates of gray dissolving frost, the reeds now partly visible below the waters.

This is why I am really here, to appreciate all this. To glimpse the back alleyways and the lean-to barns, or the blue onion dome of the tiny Orthodox church on Mäe Street. I came here to write, to find peace, breathe, to settle my jumpy nerves. I came here to walk to the top of Kõrgemäe ("High Hill") Street around 5 PM and marvel at the domino cascade of the houses.

I do care for Viljandi. It supplies feminine love, even when it seems to have vanished from my life. Enn says I shouldn't worry. He's certain my life will begin anew, as his once did. Our Enn has two children my age back in America, and now six with Kaari here in Viljandi.

"I'm still just 37 years old," I tell him another morning in the cafe, before the set arrives. "I'm too young to cash out on this life."

"Oh, you've got to start over. You absolutely have to," Enn says. "What other choice is there? Sit in a bar, drinking alone? Clogging up the back of newspapers with personal want ads?"

Hasn't he heard of the internet?

"'Seeking so-and-so?' I mean, come on, dude! You don't want to wind up like those people. Those people are losers in life," he thunders. "Total losers!"

"Losers?" I look up.

"Losers. And you don't want to be a loser. You've got to start over."

"It's not so easy. I'm a little crazy, Enn. You know that."

"We're all crazy down here. All you have to do is come to the cafe and drink my coffee. Wait until the right waitress sets her eye on you."

He finishes off this line of thought with a wink.

THE WRITER'S LIFE BEGINS

"My son went to the Waldorf preschool here, and still talks about Viljandi as if it was some kind of dream town. His childhood home where the sun was always shining, the garden with all kinds of berries and fruits." (Sofia Joons, musician who moved from Viljandi to Stockholm.)

The writer's life begins as I take my route out the door from my place on Posti Street, sun in my face, journal in pocket, early spring birds in the trees, thinking about life's switches. We conceive of life like steps or points on a map, but I think it's more like one of those action-adventure films, where you step on a trap door and tumble down a tunnel into a new realm where you are given a new identity, a new quest. That's how it's been for me here in Viljandi.

Jõeste isn't here at the café this morning, but Köler is, slumped in the corner, drinking his coffee black. But Maaker is there with his weird curly mustache and puppy dog face, standing, waiting, anxious for his take. He wears his dark hair short, but the unruly fringe just won't stay put. Because of this, it always looks as if the wind is blowing in Maaker's face.

Hedvig, the jazz singer and boisterous mother of Maaker's children, told me recently that she was annoyed with him because he refused to labor on the farm because of his profession.

"He is the man, and I have to do the work? Because he's a *guitarist*?" She rolled her eyes. 'Guitarist' might as well be 'transvestite' in Hedvig's lexicon.

I won't even get into the question of why two musicians need to live in the countryside.

"Maaker is a guitarist," I told Hedvig. "I've worked with men who used to play guitar before they ruined their fingers with hammers and saws. I don't remember Hendrix farming."

"That's just the problem with you bohemians," Hedvig scowled. "Your bohemian priorities!" and she went on and never really finished. Hedvig is full of pithy utterances. Another one of her wise sayings is, "A woman who doesn't scream at night, screams during the day." When I told her that I was writing a column about dreams, she asked if it was about "wet dreams."

When I had this scene, in my head, of a mustachioed Maaker refusing to lift a wheelbarrow on account of his guitar, my respect for him only grew. Anyone can lift a wheelbarrow and work the land and stink of *viina*, but not just anyone can play guitar well. Not just anyone can be an artist! Soon he will go to Andalusia to study flamenco music and sit with other guitarists who also look like extras from French avant-garde films patiently in a room with their instruments.

Then they will get coffee.

"Why are you standing?" I ask Maaker in the back of the cafe when I arrive.

"I just am," he shrugs. "*Niisama.*"

"Why don't you sit down like me and Köler?"

"But Enn is standing too," he nods toward the busy coffee man. "See, two of us are standing here, two are sitting. Why don't you two stand then?"

"Have it your way," I say. "By the way, Maaker, Hedvig told me you don't like to do labor on the farm because you're a guitarist. I just wanted to say that I respect you for that."

"Of course you can't do that kind of work if you want to be a good guitarist!" He shakes his face, disappointed even in the very idea.

"Hendrix wasn't a farmer."

"No, he wasn't," says Maaker, whose eyes alight again as Enn slides the hot cup to him. "Ah, thank you, sir." he says. "Neither is Clapton."

I do respect Maaker. I respect him because he is committed to his craft. He is a Viljandier, an artist. He works hard at it every day. That's why I have come here to join him. I study Maaker as he drinks and I give Enn my order. Big heavy burlap sacks are piled up in the back of the small kitchen with black inky 100% ARABICA – HONDURAS printed across them.

"Hey, sleepy head, what time did you get up?" asks Enn.

"Seven," I say.

"Seven!" he clangs the machine. "Seven! I got up at five. And I've got six, no, wait... eight kids."

"What difference does it make what time you got up? I for one got up at six," grumbles Köler over his black coffee. His voice is damp and rough-textured. "I awoke with the sunrise. Here," he motions to me with a crooked finger. "Let me give you a little Finno-Ugric advice, my boy. You should go to sleep when the sun sets and wake with the sunrise. Simple."

"I think you're right, Köler."

"Why do you keep calling me Köler? That's not even my name!"

"Because I think you look like Köler the painter."

"If you call me Köler, then who is he?" he points to Enn.

"He is another one of Viljandi's other famous dead people. Have you noticed how many important Estonians have lived in this town? Alfons Rebane used to work at the music school. The World War II officer! He fought for the Germans, ran a spy operation for MI6 after the war. He lived in Viljandi. Rebane was giving trombone lessons on the side. Can you imagine?"

"He wasn't giving trombone lessons, boy," Köler huffs. "It was a military academy then!"

One day, I even saw an old man posing for a picture beneath the plaque to Rebane on Jakobsoni Street, no taller than my chest. To think he and his generation had once blown each other to bits, all under the watchful eye of men like Eisenhower, Zhukov, and Alfons Rebane.

"Oh yeah, I met Rebane," Enn says. "When he came to New York in the Sixties. I didn't know who he was then. Another one of those World War II vets. Didn't think a thing about it."

"You met Rebane?"

"Sure, I did."

"He's long dead now."

"That's life!" Enn lets out a whistle. "Sounds like a long time. But give me eight, hundred-year-old ladies and I will give you eight hundred years. My boy's ninth birthday is tomorrow. He was born 40 years after I got wounded in Vietnam. Forty years to the day."

I take a second to marvel at this. I'm not even 40 years old.

"Where did you get wounded?"

"In the leg," he rubs at his thigh, "shrapnel."

"Was it friendly shrapnel or enemy shrapnel?"

"What do you mean 'friendly'? It's all enemy shrapnel."

"Did it come from our side or their side?"

"Oh, I don't know. Theirs, I guess."

"Was it VC? Charlie?"

"Charlie?! Are you serious? Like in those movies? Charlie? 'Uh oh. Charlie Number Three! Oh! I've got Charlie Number 10!' No, no, no, we weren't fighting any Viet Cong. We were fighting North Vietnamese regulars up on the border with Laos! Big trucks of them, covered in jungle camouflage." His eyes are suddenly more intense. He looks away. "We didn't stand a chance against them. Fighting in somebody else's jungle in their country? Can't do that."

"They should have sent in guys from the swamps if they wanted to win over there."

"Win what?" Enn's head seems to pull back on his neck like a slingshot and release. He sticks his chest out. His skin is a purple color. "Win what exactly? There was nothing to win!"

"I don't know, keep the north out? Keep South Vietnam free and democratic?"

"But it wasn't free and it wasn't democratic! It was all corrupt. It was bullshit, that's what it was. Bring democracy to the Vietnamese with the American army? Bullshit!" he turns and struts to his machine breathing heavily, then stops. "Oh, dude, you want another macchiato?"

"Sure thing."

"One more macchiato coming right up, sir. It's on the house."

Köler has been listening to this conversation all this time. He listens and he processes. Then he speaks "Have you ever seen any of the fundamental realities of life written on the walls of Viljandi?" His half- moon eyes are a bit unnerving, even creepy.

"The what?"

"The fundamental realities, boy. Of life. The fundamental realities. Have you ever seen them written anywhere on the buildings in Viljandi?"

"No."

"Good! That's because the fundamental realities of life are not written out there on the walls of Viljandi, boy! The fundamental realities of life are invisible!" Köler then laughs with great joy, as if he has, after all these years of rambling, finally grasped what has been on his mind all along. He looks wild and wicked, and a bit crazy with his old hat. But I think he's right. I do sense those fundamental realities floating in Viljandi's brisk air. They're almost everywhere.

Impossible to miss.

CHRIST IS RISEN!

*"I was there again recently and Viljandi spoke to me, pri-
mally and deeply. The stars in Viljandi are much closer
than they are anywhere else."*
*(Silver Sepp, a musician who moved from Viljandi to
Tartu.)*

The maca kicks in just as I settle into the Chef's couch and
stare at the ceiling's fine brick work, which undulates in
arches, separated into gullies above. Maca, a South American
herb for *puissance sexuelle*. If you take enough, everything is
wonderful. All spring now I've been on a binge. Trees shim-
mer with sparkling leaves. Couches heave like waves. The but-
tons of women's shirts look like candy. The Chef's ceiling is
fascinating. Most of the bricks are red, but others are purple,
and it's nice to admire the mosaic with the window open and
spring birds chirping.

"Well, they sold the apartment, so I had to move out," says
the Chef, pacing as the hot teapot of green *meliss* sets or, as
the Estonians say, *tõmbab* (pulls), like the water is tugging all
the vital essence from the leaves. "But you know what, I actually like this new place. My new place is even better." A weird
chuckle. Pacing, always pacing. Our restless divorcee doesn't
sound very happy at all. No, our man Chef is still in the throes
of his crisis or collapse, his beautiful catastrophe. He's grown

his hair, pulled it up in one of those Chinese warrior buns. We go to yoga religiously now. There we study under the supervision of the great instructor General Ly, who marches among the devotees and stretches them out and plays devotionals to krishna. Yoga is also the final resort of the divorced man. For there are many women stretching at *jooga* too.

Many.

"Going to yoga again this week?" he asks.

"Of course."

"*Tubli.* Here," he sets out the tea cups. "Fresh *meliss*, with some honey. Enjoy!"

This is on the second floor of a renovated factory building behind the hostel by the beach. It looks innocent enough, but according to Orav, the husky-voiced entrepreneur who fixed it up, and runs a gas station on the edge of town, the area of the sports stadium by the lake was once a sheep pasture, and this adjacent building was a slaughterhouse. When they renovated it, they found sacks full of horns in the attic. Now it's been repurposed with all modern conveniences. Central heating. Wifi. A bathroom covered in tile. IKEA furniture, plus a great sauna downstairs. Once a week, we have a very serious "sauna meeting" where we commiserate. Different men filter in and out of the weekly sauna meetings. Even Pepi the Argentinian comes sometimes. This has taken on an almost religious significance. It merits anthropological study.

"This place is like ... Swedish, you know," says the Chef, now sipping his *meliss*. "Modern. No wood heating, no damn ecofriendly renovation work! I used to have a list of things to do. Here I can live just like I would live in Sweden," he drums his fingers, "but with all the benefits of living here in town. Because if I actually lived in Sweden, I would just go out of my mind with boredom."

All I can manage to do is grunt once in agreement, but I can't really hear him as he goes on about his tea, or whatever, because this wonderful, terrifying feeling has set inside of me and I just have to let it take over. All that beautiful brickwork wrapped up in this springtime yearning.

"What's up with you today?" he asks.

I just grin.

"Maca? Again? You know you're turning into a real lunatic, man! People in Viljandi are talking about you, you know. They see you walking down the street laughing at your own jokes."

"If this is Estonia's San Francisco, then I'm entitled to some psychedelic experiences."

"What does it feel like?"

I'm not sure what feeling it is, but it's on me, and I feel loose and creative, full of hope and optimism, but scared too. Like the bricks in the ceiling, lots of light colors, with some dark.

I try to write at the cafe, but mostly I am a nuisance. It is here where I meet the Designer again, who is actually trying to work despite interruptions from the fool who claims to be in love with her. The Designer has been closed to me for months. We used to meet, we used to embrace! There was once a lingering aroma of love wherever we walked. There is only misunderstandings now. I am not sure where, or how, it went wrong. I'm not even sure what I want. Besides, her cat doesn't even like me.

"But he doesn't like you," the Designer informs me over coffee at the cafe.

"He actually does."

"No. I've seen him with other men. He likes them, but he doesn't like you."

"Not true."

"Do you really want to have this argument now?"

"He purrs with me."

"That's just because he wants something. He actually doesn't like you."

"You know he likes me. But you are telling me he doesn't like me in order to hurt me."

"He doesn't like you."

The Designer is in a good mood though because she's working on new projects. She is unfazed by my neurotic episodes. She even displays an image of a man wearing a hat that folds at the edges, but only for a second. It looks like something a Tibetan shepherd would wear.

The Designer has been creative.

"There it is. That's my brand." She hides it away. Then the Designer ventures a question. "But what are you working on now, *Härra* Petrone?"

"My next column is actually due, and I have no idea what to write about."

"You should write about grief," she says. "Get all your sadness out into one new column. Call it the last bit of sorrow, or something like that."

I pick through this idea a bit. I have been trying to write a new way, and maybe this will be an opportunity to do it. In the past, I would merely go for jokes, comic set-ups, humor. But what I really want to achieve is what some of the more innovative musicians in the 1960s called "images in sound". I want to express images in words, yet not in a fully conscious way, where the meanings are curated and explained. I want the images to communicate meaning without any explanation, to stand up for themselves.

When it comes to my own sorrow, I have the image of two mountain climbers tied together. One falls off an edge, and the other decides to cut the rope to save himself. It's that terror in the midst of freefall that I want to express to the reader. These thoughts I jot down in my notebook as the Designer works on across from me. New ideas!

I wouldn't have reached for the concept if I hadn't been prodded though. I am grateful. This is how we work together in silence. Two Viljandi artists. Then, at precisely 2 PM, Jalmar enters the cafe.

Somehow in my months of pining after the Designer and working at the cafe by drinking macchiatos and hanging with Köler, Maaker, and Jõeste, I have managed to avoid the folk musicians. But Jalmar cannot be avoided! He is the king of the Viljandi folk musicians and may very well be the king of the Folk Music Festival itself. I have never been able to figure out what's wrong with Jalmar. As far as I know, the guitarist and singer for Zetod and Trad.Attack! has never overdosed on drugs, been jailed, or committed to the Jämejala Psychiatric Clinic down the street. Yet he produces excellent music, even if these well-worn hallmarks of talent aren't there.

He's just fine. *Tal on kõik hästi.*

The Designer rises from the table and embraces him as soon as he enters. It's a warm, lingering embrace out of a French soap opera. This woman who will not even shake my hand! I pretend to ignore it, but I seethe with envy. Then she settles into her seat again and to her work.

"Jalmar, what's wrong with you?" I ask as he orders a coffee.

"What's wrong with me?" Jalmar shoots me an amused but implausible look and takes his seat with the day's *Sakala* newspaper. I can never tell if Jalmar is serious or joking. Many of the folk musicians walk this same ironic line. Villu from Curly Strings comes to the cafe just like Jalmar. He reads the newspaper just like him and drinks his coffee, probably the same kind. They are the same, of the same build. They are all in on the joke. But what is the joke? Sometimes I see the folk musicians eating alone out in the yard. They sit at the most distant table. Jalmar and Sandra are there from Trad.Attack!. Then Karoliina from Tintura. Then Villu comes, then Eeva from Curly Strings. On occasion, they are joined by Taavet the Strings' bassist. They whisper.

"I don't think you understand me," I now tell Jalmar, who eyes me over his newspaper. The maca effect has worn off from earlier, but I still feel loose. From my bag, I retrieve a book I have been reading on British rock music. "See here. Pete Townshend from The Who – drug addict. Pink Floyd's Syd Barrett – drug addict. David Bowie – also a drug addict. But you?"

"What is it that you're trying to say, *härra*?"

"It's time you got with the program, Jalmar!" I slam the book down. "The writing is on the wall. You need drugs, young Jalmar. Drugs! It's time you became a real artist like David Bowie!"

"Just give me time," he gestures me away, chuckling nervously. "More time."

Jalmar may have a pleasant, country-boy face but there is a strange shine in his stare that suggests the madness common among the peculiar Seto types in the country's southeast – Jalmar's people – who play *karmoška* accordions all day and feast on loaves of *sõir* cheese and gulp fermented *kali* or kvass out of dirty old jars. This is the devil's music he plays when Zetod headlines the Viljandi Folk Music Festival in the summer. He comes out to the lip of the stage in his pin-striped trousers and cap and wrestles mammoth guitar riffs from his instrument. The people all mass before him and he blesses his followers. Folk is like a great pagan church.

Jalmar is its high priest.

Before he goes, Jalmar invites me to Paabel's last concert, to be held tonight.

"And Zetod will also be playing," he winks just before slipping out the door.

The Paabel concert lasts three and a half hours. It's held in the Ait's main hall. There are three stages inside the room, a male choir, and Jalmar does come up toward the end with the rest of Zetod, dressed in their noble white folk costumes, to sing a few verses in honor of this great band. Paabel has a big sound. It has melodies too, some are catchy, some are melancholic. But what takes you over is the ocean of guitars and bagpipes, contrabass, and heavy drums.

I don't understand what they sing about in unison but I feel special to be at the concert. There are few other outsiders here. The Argentinian is in the corner dancing furiously, as is the Australian who used to work at Eesti Post. I feel I can never describe what I see in the concert to anyone who isn't from here, and even if they were here, they wouldn't understand its meaning. I barely understand what they are singing. All of these songs in some dialect. Can anyone who is not from Viljandi understand this stuff? But there is more to the community than just music. There is that sense of camaraderie, of belonging. There is that sense of being part of one family.

During a break, Merit, the Lionness of Fellin, finds me and summons me to the window in the cafe to look at the sunset. Here she tells me of her childhood in Männimäe and holds my hand.

"We used to sit in the windows, just like this one, and watch the sunset, just like this."

I want to melt into the rays of the sun with her. I haven't felt love in months. No one hugs me. No one touches me. When I complain about it, I am told I should go prostitute myself on Tinder. The feel of a woman's hand while watching the sunset is something worth writing about.

At the afterparty, I sit beside a different kind of woman who smells like smoke and who drapes an arm around my shoulder. Now there are more weird people around, and Jalmar is the DJ. He winks to me as the woman moves in. "So," she says and slides her hand down my thigh.

Then, I tell her I have to go use the toilet, and flee into the dark.

On Kirsimägi, I take a seat at a bench. I'm all alone and the birds are still singing. I shiver as I survey the lake. For a moment, I think I see something moving down there across the surface of the lake. It looks like a tiny boat, but it's just there for a second and then it's gone. What a weird evening. I blink in confusion. Tomorrow, I decide, I will cook up the biggest maca fix yet.

Later, I come up Mäe Street with the church bells clanging, snow in my eyes. That's when I realize that it's Orthodox Easter Sunday. There is a military immediacy to the way the bells ring on Easter. I see the puffs of smoke rising. Even the Orthodox church on Mäe Street is heated by firewood.

In the Soviet era, it was not a church, of course. They used it as a morgue, and the building across the street was a hospital. The hostel on Väike Street was a maternity ward. My children's mother was born there ages ago in that parallel Leninist universe. So was Teet Margna, the famous TV host, and even Mart Laar, the statesman. Outside, the priest leads the procession, as the believers huddle around him. They cross themselves every time he invokes the sacred name of "Christus," and I recall how not long ago I had done the same. I even joined the Greek Church. Back then, I had prayed for a miracle. Now I have to ask, was this all part of it?

I remove my hat from my head and stand with the others, cross myself in the cold as the priest proclaims – first in Old Slavonic, and then in Estonian – "Christ is Risen! Christ is Risen!" A female chorus answers him. Peace comes into my heart with the flicker of the candles and with the weave of the songs, but also desperate memories. When the priest leads the procession back into the church, I start to move with them, but my feet won't let me follow the flock inside.

I know I should follow them, but my feet just won't let me.

A MIDSUMMER SECRET

"I call Viljandi a ghost town, because that's what it's become. When I was a kid, it was full of people in the streets. Today, the streets are empty. There's hardly anybody there!"
(Brad Jurjens, a guitarist who moved from Viljandi to Los Angeles.)

Coming back from Rivo's cabin on *Jaanipäev*, the lights of Viljandi blinking over the lake. The town that once signaled to me rebirth has become a ghost town at Midsummer. Each building is like a tombstone, bleak and ominous. Strewn between the tombstones are cobwebs – laundry lines, satellite dishes. The streets are barren and empty, everybody *maale*, to the countryside. How could this be? All winter we waited for summer. All through the winter we waited, and then when the light began to grow, we knew that something good must lay ahead, but that thing was a cold thing. The streets in June are awash in rainwater. The sky is pewter gray. Midsummer is therefore a great loss. The loss of hope that life here could go another way. There is no new love here. Only the lingering blue-orange afterglow of the death of dreams.

It was over a month ago that the Designer sat me down on a park bench and informed me that whatever residual romantic feelings that I felt for us would never materialize in any situation. She was exhausted by my relentless romantic pursuit of her. It was driving me mad as well. Time and time again, I was reminded of a dog we once had who would go berserk everytime he saw a squirrel outside the window. Every time he saw a squirrel, he ran face-first into the glass, only to fall back dazed, hollering in pain. This was me. She was outside. Still, I kept running into the glass.

Why did I keep running headfirst into the glass?

"I just don't think I'm the right person for you," she said and pulled her jacket tighter, as if I might strike her. The sight of her cringing before my presence – I am nearly twice her size – only filled me with disgust. When a man's lust consumes him, he is capable of terrible things.

Yet, was it always so terrible?

On her 30th birthday in May I had brought the Designer three sweet potatoes, one for each decade. I couldn't fathom why I did it – I didn't really expect anything – other than that something inside me *compelled* me to. It was as if there was a little blue ghost inside me stirring. As if I was somehow possessed. But, what else could you really expect for three sweet potatoes?

"I didn't really expect anything anyway," I said on the bench. "What could I expect?"

She looked up at me, a bit confused.

"Are you sure?"

"I'm sure."

"Are you sure you're sure?"

"I'm sure I'm sure."

"Good," she said. "Because I just don't like to get attached."

This last line surprised me. There was obviously a lot going on beneath the surface of this otherwise coiffed and polished presence, a person who could make a bag full of textiles from some second-hand store shine resplendent, who soldiered on with creative projects without missing a beat. There was so much going on, but a line like that was protected by multiple rings of castle walls, and I seriously doubted I could ever breach any of these thick fortified walls to the honey of her heart. The dog ran into the glass. He saw the squirrel, but he couldn't reach it.

I looked down at her and her pale hands. The way she shivered in the spring chill. She was just a marvel of Estonianness. She likes sewing and knitting. Some *handsa* from the bottle. The sauna. Nude lake swimming. Hunting for berries and mushrooms. Doesn't like to get attached!

"I don't try to do romantic things. Something just makes me do them," I said.

She eyed me as if I was very, very strange.

"I sincerely hope you didn't move to Viljandi for me," she said at last.

"Not at all," I said. "I came here to become a better writer."

"Good. Because that would have been very stupid of you if you did that."

"Why?"

"Because I'm leaving."

"Wait. You're leaving? But why? Where are you going?"

"I got a new job. I'm moving to Tallinn at the end of the summer."

I said nothing. But the weight of being left again crushed me inside.

I thought she was gone. Yet as I near the crest of a hill coming back from Rivo's cabin on Saint John's Day, the Designer again beckons me. There's an eerie light over the lake through the trees. A smoky haze. Fires burning everywhere. Viljandi looks as if it has been possessed by the devil.

"Are you around?" she texts.

"Why?"

"Nothing."

"What is it?"

"I need a guy with a car."

"I'll be there in five minutes."

"Are you in Viljandi?"

"Viiratsi."

"Forget it."

"I'll come."

"You don't have to."

"I'm coming anyway."

"No need."

"I'll be there in five minutes."

When I arrive, she's sitting in the dirt, her arms over her legs. Her bicycle stands against the tree, and there is a huge sack of cloth set down beside it. She's moving again, this time to the *Lossi Kommuun* on Lossi Street. This will be her third residence in Viljandi in less than a year. In the spring, she moved to the Koidu Street apartment, but has only stayed there for a few months. She plans to stay at the *Kommuun* and save up money for the move to Tallinn at the end of the summer. The Designer won't even look at me. It feels as if there has been some kind of accident.

"Okay, lady, where is it?" I say, bounding out of the car like Indiana Jones. I feel like tossing the bag over my shoulders and then scooping her up in my arms like King Kong.

Somehow, I still think that if I perform enough manly Estonian feats of strength for her, such as carrying her bags, assembling her furniture, stacking her firewood, standing atop a steaming sauna *kerris*, or dancing the *kaerajaan* (a folk dance), it will stoke the fires of her heart and she will see me as a real and worthy man, instead of as a rodent. But every move of mine toward her is off and out of sequence. All is wrong.

"No, no," she recoils as I come closer. "I am *not* dealing with you when you're like this!"

"Like what?"

"Like you are. Just look at you!"

"Then what do you need help with, goddamnit?"

She gestures weakly to the bag.

"Don't tell me you were actually trying to take that bag on your bike. Are you crazy?"

She doesn't react well to this. In the spring I had brought her firewood with my car but she had insisted at first that she could haul it with her bike. She has fit chairs on there. The bike is her superpower, she says, but it's still not superpower enough to get this maniac out of her life.

I hoist the bag on my shoulder, toss it in the trunk, and gesture to the door. "Get in."

The Designer slips into the car, hesitant. We drive down to a street by the lake. It's a silent tense ride while she stares out of the window. This small person. Sometimes she's here, but more often, she isn't. She flickers in, briefly, but then she's gone. Tonight, she is a stranger to me.

After I drop the bag at someone's door, she then turns to me and grumbles, "You're my hero." Then she gets back in the car. She's tired of it. Once again, she has realized that she's on the net. She struggles against it. She writhes back and forth in agony like a mermaid caught by a trawler. She deserts me, and then I desert her. Yet we are stuck together. Up the hill in silence. The brooding, the malcontent. "I'm so tired of your drama," she says and rides away on her bike.

Again, the dog smashed face-first into the glass.

She cycles off into the dark and for a few moments all is peace. Yet back in the apartment, I receive another mysterious Midsummer's message. This one says, "Come over right now."

It's from the woman down the street, a local teacher I know from the cafe. I've been to her place on a few occasions, and sometimes it's just been us chatting, a few times drinking wine with friends. But what could she possibly want from me after midnight on Saint John's Day? When I get there minutes later, I see the teacher is wasted, sprawled on the carpet. An empty wine bottle stands on the table. Incense burns. Candles are flickering. There is an Estonian flag.

"Here, here, come," she says, "take off your pants and shirt."

My first instinct is to run, but a curious voice tells me to stay and see what happens. It will make you a better writer, the curious voice says.

"An Italian," she coos, rubbing my chest and then stroking below. "It's so exotic. Anyone can have a Swede or a Russian, you know, anyone, but an Italian! Look at all that thick dark hair you've got under there. Why, it's like you've got another shirt under your shirt!"

The act is urgent and desperate. Inside, I'm spinning and spinning, and all I can think of though is Miss Cloud from my birthday, that misplaced girl from the north coast. I haven't heard from her in months now, and I have no idea what became of her. Yet, out of all these daily nightmares, she's the only one left with whom I feel any degree of warmth or safety. Too bad she cannot be tracked down. For Miss Cloud only appears when she wishes. Every night she's out sleeping on another couch. If I could only disappear with Miss Cloud, I think. Forget myself. Forget all my dreams. Forget everything. Fold myself up into her warm embrace. For what else could love ever be at this point? Tender feelings? Shared dreams? An emotional connection? Nothing is special or sacred anymore. There is no love anymore. There are no more dreams.

The only real love then must be hot flesh, flesh that folds up in your hands. Let everything else go.

Let everything else burn.

"Oh," the teacher says suddenly.

"What?"

"There's someone else."

"What are you talking about?"

"You're thinking about someone else."

"No, I'm not."

"Who is she?"

"Who is who?"

"Who is she?"

"There's no one else."

"Is it that singer I read about in *Kroonika*?"

"No."

"There's someone else. I can see it. I can see it in your eyes right now."

"You're crazy."

"You've been thinking about her the whole time you've been with me, haven't you?"

"No."

"You're in love with her, aren't you?"

"No."

"Tell me now."

"No."

"Yes, you are," she jabs a finger in my chest. "I can see it all in your eyes."

"No."

"Just tell me her name," she demands climbing on top of me and rocking her hips.

"There's no one."

"Yes, there is!"

"Stop it."

"I said tell me her name now!"

"No!"

"Tell me her name now, damnit!"

"There's no one else!"

"Stop lying to me!"

"There's no one else!"

"Yes, there is! You lying bastard!" Then she leans in more closely, puts her nose to mine. "You're soaked in her like a Christmas cake is soaked in rum."

Home through the streets of Viljandi, the horizon a menacing orange. It's midsummer still. Somewhere out there, the parties are still going on. Good-natured Rivo is still at his cabin at the lake, drinking and boasting. Rivo, with his rooster crop of dark hair, his good guy face. The *joie de vivre*, the laughter echoing. The satisfaction of the St. John's fire (*Jaanituli*). I should have stayed there! I should have stayed with Rivo!

Instead, I am in godforsaken satanic Viljandi. Someone is setting off fireworks. Or are those gunshots? *The Russians again?* Every century or so, they show up and burn Viljandi to the ground. The marauding troops of Ivan the Terrible. The torch-bearing henchmen of Peter the Great. Any time I hear fireworks in Viljandi, I assume they have returned. The sounds explode in the air. Then my phone vibrates. It's a message from the Designer.

"Don't contact me again!"

"Fine!"

"Not one more word! I have had enough of your drama in my life!"

"I don't love you anymore anyway!"

"You do it to yourself," she writes and is gone.

At home, I stand before my apartment's furnace, the one that once gave me such hope, and tear out the pages of my journal. One by one, I rip them clean from the binding. I strike a match and the papers begin to smoke. The run-in with the teacher is already a faint memory and all I can think of is the girl on the bike now. I tried so hard to be an Estonian man with her, to be "just a guy with a car." She asked for nothing more. Just a lift. Simple.

Yet once again I am failing. I try and I am failing. I'm not like the kind of man they want. The reliable, easy type who fills the day on renovation projects, makes the money, fixes the roof, saws the wood. Tells them he loves them, but sparingly, and expects nothing but a bowl of soup in return. No, I am not one of these Estonians. I am one of these "womanly" Latin men. I used to think it was an insult to be called womanly, but I feel in these moments more manly, and womanlier, than any of these people.

This country. It's so cute and so cursed. And Viljandi is the core of the disease. It's spreading from here like a poisonous flower. Nearby there is a village called Õisu. "Blossom."

I feed each journal page to the blaze. Every word written turns black and vanishes into ash. *You Estonians want a damn Saint John's Day bonfire? Then leap over this goddamn bonfire!*

Then I burn its cover.

I thought it would all be so easy. Just move to Viljandi, be a writer, fall in love again. It seemed like such a simple story. But my simple story has just gone up again in furnace flames.

The next morning, I see Köler on my way to the cafe. An overcast morning of haze and dust. I don't even have to look in his direction before he smiles at me. He already knows everything. Everyone in this town already knows.

"Oh, you Southerners are all the same," says the strange man from beneath the broad brim of his hat. He has a slow but purposeful gait, like the frontier gunslinger that he is. There is a knowing gleam in his eyes. I wonder if Köler witnessed the scene in the park, or if he watched me through the windows as the woman pounded her fist. *"Tell me her name! Tell me her name!"*

"What are you talking about?"

"You Italians come up here and you fall in love with our women because they are so white and beautiful. But our Finno-Ugric women are cold fish. You crave warmth, you crave love, but you'll never get it." Köler shivers and chuckles. There is a joyous cynicism to that laugh. He knows that yearning, that longing for a summer warmth that never seems to come.

Köler shakes his head sadly at me as we enter the cafe for our daily victuals. He will have his Americano. I will have my macchiato, *tume röst*. He grips my shoulder, glares into my eyes.

"They can't all be so bad," I mumble.

"My boy," answers Köler. "They are as slippery and treacherous as the Ural Mountains."

A HIKE AROUND THE LAKE

After that, on a July day, I decide to hike around the lake to ease my weary mind. It's a 12-kilometer, two-to-three-hour investment and you start out down by the public beaches, then wind your way along the newish condos toward the land bridge that separates Viljandi from the hills of Viiratsi. There are sights here to brighten one's spirits. The most surprising discoveries are the beaches on the other side, down paths. Little patches of yellow sand, with a few adventurous sunbathers who know where to look, and then those fields that lead to the horse farm at Sammuli. There's always something so hopeful about those Sammuli horses.

Somewhere near here though, on June 10th, a 17-year-old girl was murdered by a jealous man. As I pass through the terrain, I search for the spot, but find no trace, no flowers, nothing. It seems so sad to me that a young life could be snuffed out like that, all for unrequited love, and leave no mark behind, just the flutter of birds on the timber, or the rainwater in the grass. I feel ashamed then for the longing I have felt for various women in my life, and how besieged they are by this relentless aching want, the savage want of man, so terrible it leads some to kill.

Sadder still is that not one person in Viljandi has told me about the murder. You would think the town would have been awash in it. I only found out about it from reading *Postimees*.

There is this sense though that nothing bad ever happens in Viljandi, and if it happens, then it isn't real. Viljandi is the home of Folk, of the Academy, of Ugala. There are no murders in Viljandi, or rather there are two Viljandis. The real one and the one that exists in your mind.

I drift on around the lake, admiring the horses, forgetting about everything before. Eventually I make it to the other side, and the paths rise through the towering pines of Männimäe, then the hills that roll toward the apartments, the Castle Ruins, and the Old Town.

There are all kinds of secrets back here. It is at the base of a hill beyond Männimäe that I come across a marker to the masses of people buried following the uprisings of 1905. I don't know the circumstances of their deaths, or how many are buried down here. The grass around the memorial is wet and the woods are somehow darker. I don't like how the mud sticks to my shoes, as if it could pull me down. Every step is wet near the stone and makes an eerie sucking sound.

I have no idea how many dead people are sleeping down there below me.

I suppose I have been seeking, all this time, a new woman to reset the clock of my heart, and for some unknown reason the clock had been synchronized to the Designer. But she has her own worries and we are friends, just friends, after all. Yet all summer, I feel that hungry, nagging, aching void.

Even though I am writing better now, and people who know me say I am writing better, and my column that used my new "images in words" approach was so well received that people have come up to me in restaurants all around the country just to compliment me on it, I am still not satisfied in my new life.

After a long period of self-imposed exile and only eating at home, I somewhat sheepishly return to the Green House, where I am welcomed back by Kaari in her apron with her rosy cheeks and straw-colored hair. Kaari with her wonderful warm humor.

For nearly two decades or more, Kaari and Enn have been husband and wife. She has given him six children, and holds forth as the den mother of the cafe life. Enn, although born abroad, is still Estonian at heart and cannot sit still. He is either coming or going, and usually he has a piece of wood in his hands. In addition to the cafe, they have a farm outside of Viljandi, a town apartment, and even a piece of land in Põlvamaa somewhere. There was even that most common of Estonian stories: the log cabin in Põlvamaa that had to be transferred to the property in Viljandimaa, and reassembled like Legos. This is the local life: log cabins, chickens, building.

Kaari is never in want of company at the cafe, and is often seen sitting in the company of many good friends. She has a jolly countenance and wise but childlike blue eyes. There is a playfulness, a girlishness in her character. She just seems to love and embrace life deeply. She and her friends probably know everything about everyone in town, and I am sure they know everything about me. Kaari is a few years older than me and takes on a concerned older sister role at times. I've forgotten that in the eyes of most of these people I am a "divorced man", which to most of them sounds like I just got out of prison. Most regard a divorced man as having done something unseemly. Maybe he robbed a bank or even an ice cream truck. But the sight of me sauntering in after a long hike around the lake, the look on my face, makes her more concerned.

"But Justin," says Kaari, "Where have you been all this summer?!"

"I've been eating at home mostly."

"But you shouldn't be alone," says Kaari, frowning. "You must come back. Be with us!"

And so, I return to the Green House Cafe, under the concerned, somewhat sorrowful watch of Kaari, who is not only a mother to six rambunctious children, but a mother to us all.

It is there on a fragrant afternoon, after a tropical rainfall, that I see the Designer again, sitting all alone at a table out in the yard. At first, I am terrified that I will do something wrong, even by looking at her, but then I notice those eyes and that all-knowing smile of hers. Then I stride over to her and kiss her on the top of her fuzzy head.

"Your hair is thick and wooly," I say. "Like a sheep's fleece."

"You really are so annoying. You're lucky I'm even talking to you."

I only half-smile in response.

"Oh," she yawns and stretches like a cat, "I'm *so* tired today." She had been out with friends. They had bounced between Mulks, Romaan, and any place in Viljandi where youth congregate. The Designer still looks beautiful today, but in a faded, exhausted way.

"Why were you so mad at me on Midsummer's?" I ask.

"Because you were acting like an asshole."

"Yes, I was dumb, wasn't I?"

"Yes, you were."

"Really, really dumb."

"Yes, you really, really were."

"But if it's okay with you, can we still be friends?"

The Designer squints at me after I speak, as if she hasn't understood it quite correctly. "Oh, you really are so stupid, *Härra* Petrone," she says. "So stupid. *Nii loll.*"

MISS CLOUD

This morning Viljandi Town was covered with a dense fog, which also wrapped itself around the taller apartment buildings of Viljandi. The fog created fabulous views of the Old Town.
(Sigrid Koorep, "Sakala" newspaper, 2017)

A moist, gray October day. *Udune,* as they say, or foggy. Fog off the lake, in the streets, in your hair. Fog creeping up ghost-like from the floorboards, swirling roundabout your head. Shadows on the way to school and work. Shadows on bicycles. Shadows pushing baby carriages. On some foggy mornings like this, local women descend the stairs of Trepimägi and go swimming in the lake, even in October. They enjoy the beauty of Estonia's San Francisco as the mist rolls in and the sun burns the fog away. I awake feeling groggy and middle aged and go to the cafe to work, Köler's creaky voice at the door ringing behind me as I take my seat in front.

"This is as good as it will get for you, boy. It's all downhill from here!"

He already sees it. He already sees me turning into a bitter old man.

Around this time there's a full moon, surreal yellow above a dew-drenched autumn. I awake again feeling groggy and middle-aged and then I wish secretly for the return of Miss Cloud, the strange girl who had walked me down to the lake on my birthday. "If only Miss Cloud was here." I want to disappear into her, disappear into warmth and euphoria, to disappear into femaleness. This is the form that this imaginary comfort takes alongside me, fitting, firm, and congruent. Then, to my surprise, as I sit sipping my drink and trying to work at the cafe, Miss Cloud stumbles through the door. It's as if I have summoned her by thinking about her. Imagine that. I think that she will disappear elsewhere into the cafe. Instead, she comes and sits beside me.

Miss Cloud has been sleeping on a couch at her friend's apartment on Lossi Street. She carries with her a big backpack and moves from place to place. Today Viljandi, later Rapla. Miss Cloud used to rent a place on Sauna Street in Tallinn with a scheme to open a massage therapy business, and even bought the brushes and paint to fix it up, but she spent most of her time there dreaming and eyeing the walls that needed so much work and then having another nap.

Her face in the morning light is lush and fleshy. Her manners are hard-elbowed and rough. She is a tough Ingrian girl,

I think, not one of these meek, hesitant Estonian girls. For centuries, the Cloud family has called a tiny village near Narva in Ida-Virumaa county home. Legend is that she was one of a handful of Estonians in her graduating class in Narva. She didn't mind. "My brain is chill speaking other languages," she says. I love how she refers to her mind as if it's something separate from herself. "And, why should I pay rent for an apartment I don't use?" she harrumphs. "I'm on the road!"

Miss Cloud is annoyed by my line of questions, but I know she sometimes can be sweet. Once in the summer she wrote to me how she ventured to the water's edge to wash her chocolate hair in Tallinn Bay. These little scraps of softness from her are like pieces of chocolate. She doesn't care for my yearning heart though. She's more focused on trying to digest all that has happened in the past few days. "It's been so crazy! Oh my God!" She shuts her eyes. I decide I don't need to know. She especially wants to recall the most important parts of last night's dream. This is of the utmost importance. The server slides her a turmeric latte, a cup of "golden milk" as Miss Cloud calls it, but she doesn't touch it, and doesn't even know it's been placed before her. All because of the dream! "Would you please be quiet. I'm trying to remember my dream!"

"What happened in the dream?"

"Would you shut up please!"

"Okay, okay."

She hums a bit to herself, then cocks her head to the left, then a bit to the right. Her face contorts as she reviews parts of the vision. She drifts slowly to one side, then back to the other. "There was some kind of prison," she whispers. "But the guards in there weren't really human." Her breathing becomes more rapid. "And then, when I tried to escape, I remember I touched one of the guard's faces, and it was soft like skin but all rubbery too. And then when we got out, we were in some tropical garden. It was like another world! Then the scene just turned, like the page of a book. Just like someone had just turned the page of a book. Oh, it was all so beautiful there." A hot tear runs down her cheek. "Don't mind me," she says, now opening her wet eyes and staring at me over the table. "My dreams often make me cry. Sometimes I wake up sobbing."

I am mesmerized.

We are not alone here in the cafe, though. We have been joined by my friend the Chef.

"Hey, do you still like her?" he whispers to me when she leaves to use the toilet.

"Yes. I do."

"Well, I like her too now," he says. "She has such interesting energy today. *Energia.*"

"I don't have any intentions toward her," I shrug. "Nobody owns anyone."

The Chef's work has been lumpy as of late, but he's still living in a renovated slaughterhouse down by the lake. His latest gig has been mixing cement for the reconstruction of a castle wall at nearby Mustla. It's a historical preservation project. Unique opportunities open up for the recently divorced.

Each morning he rises early and makes himself an additional breakfast sandwich because the work is so hard and he's tired of the schnitzel and potatoes at the Mustla tavern. "I have to pay five more euros every day, just to keep working. It doesn't make any sense." A TV crew was recently out to the castle and they interviewed the head contractor. "It's hard work," he told them. "The hardest work. Why, I think we have the hardest men working this job." *Kõige kõvemad mehed.* This amuses the Chef to no end. He replays the clip for us and plays it again. "Listen, listen. '*The hardest men …,*'" and he can't stop laughing and neither can Miss Cloud. "Hey, hey, let's go back to my place," he announces to us. "We can have a pot of tea."

Outside he whispers. "Is it really okay if you two come down the hill to my apartment? Don't want to disturb your little date. Your *deidike.*"

"I thought you two were on the date," I say.

He laughs that disturbed little laugh of his and says, "Maybe we are, maybe we are." Down the hill he grabs a bunch of wilting flowers from an overgrown garden and smacks the girl on the arm with them two times. Is that some kind of Swedish love gesture? I wonder. Then he does it again! That energy, that weird, weird energy. Inside, he's at ease in his kitchen, where all is in order. He's got some jazz playing and he's making her baked apple with cinnamon and ice cream. Then the pot of *meliss* tea, the honey set in small, perfect ceramic dishes. What a bastard.

Miss Cloud is enjoying it though, swinging her legs in the chair and recounting how she once tried whale soup in Norway and how pungent and chewy the flesh was. *Vaala-*

supp! She's laughing while the tea is setting, and the Chef is pacing. I am away at a distant on the couch with a guitar. The sight of the two of them laughing. I can't take it anymore because I am *kade*. Jealous. Therefore, I announce my departure. "Wait, where are you going?" asks Miss Cloud.

"There were some lambs by the Castle Ruins in the summer," I inform them. "Just want to see if they are still there."

Outside there is drizzle and fog and I walk to the lambs. The Castle Ruins were for a long time a pasture for shepherds, even into the last century, and you can see grainy black-and-white photographs of those days and the Viljandi shepherds, and recently sheep were reintroduced with big bales of hay. It really gives Viljandi a natural, lived-in feeling, like an open-air museum. But the lambs today are all gone and there are no more bales of hay, though the fencing is there. I head over to one of the larger trees alongside the path and rest my body against it.

I don't like feeling so vulnerable. I also don't like the feeling that I am jealous of my best friend. I just don't like this thing. He's got baked apples and tea. What do I have? All I have are words.

"You're a fine writer," someone had once told me. "But, that's all you are." A deep breath. A misty release. I suppose I will have to go back there. With hands in my pockets, I trudge back.

"*Härra* Petrone," says Miss Cloud when I reenter, my coat soaked in moisture. "Come over here! Have you ever noticed how wonderful the ceiling is here?"

She stands in the corridor looking straight up. It is a wonderful ceiling. The same one I had studied in the springtime when I was on a psychedelic maca binge. All of the undulating brick work. The purples and reds. The bricks arch into gullies that run the length of the ceiling.

"Do you see those deeper parts?" She points them out to me. "They are as wide as a person. Can you imagine? Can you imagine that if the ceiling was the floor then we could sleep in those little brick gullies!? Can you imagine, all curled up with blankets? That would be so cool! Oh, if only the ceiling was the floor, and the floor was the ceiling. Wouldn't it be so wonderful?"

I can't even answer, I feel such love-joy. Maybe the girl called Miss Cloud is my soulmate. Maybe the Designer was right to introduce us. The Chef is at the stovetop scratching his eye. When she goes to use the bathroom, he pulls me aside in the corridor by the wet coats.

"Why did you leave me alone with her?" he says. "Can't you see she's schizophrenic?"

"I was jealous! You've got the jazz, the baked apple. What are you pulling?"

"Nothing. That's just who I am. I'm a good host!"

"Well, if you want to be with her, then just be with her. Go ahead. Take her to bed."

"Are you kidding me, man?"

"Go ahead then. See if I care. The bedroom's right over there."

"You're kidding."

"I don't trust you."

"Are you serious? I just thought she was an interesting person!"

"Never trust a chef!"

"You're ridiculous."

I say nothing, but now I'm the one with a tear in the eye.

"Oh," he grins. "You're in love with her, aren't you?"

Miss Cloud hugs the Chef goodbye and we leave together. We hike up the hill, which is called Liiva Street, or Sand Street, and is really made of sand. All of the houses here are built into the hill, and the street is at a 45-degree angle. It seems impossible to navigate with a car and it's not easy on foot, either going up or coming down. There are good views though, including the playground where we sat together on my birthday, which already seems like an eternity ago.

Miss Cloud has a fine red raincoat. She keeps looking at a contract for a job. She's studying it with a strange intensity. Her hood is drawn together, so that only her face is visible.

"I like your coat," I say after some time. "You look like a real Karelian *babushka*."

Her face recoils deeper into the coat. "You think I look like some kind of *grandmother*?"

"Yes," I say, touching her hood. "You look like a very pretty Karelian grandmother."

"I guess I will have to take it as a compliment."

"Where are you going next?"

"To the train," she says. "To Rapla."

"Do you need a ride?"

"No. I prefer to walk."

"Good, because my car's a mess anyway and I didn't want to take you."

This girl. She's a decade younger than me. It makes no sense to hunt her down. Let her live her dream of couches and adventures. I have my own life. Wasn't I supposed to be a writer? Maybe she will come back again. Sometimes I do feel like a hungry sea lion growling at the sea. When the sea finally tosses a fish in your direction, it hits you so hard you can barely think at all. You just lie there dazed, sniffing at the fish.

THE CAFE CLUB

"Viljandi is a perfect small town. It's cute and quaint, and you don't have to look far for coffee. In Võru, where I'm from, you have to hunt for good coffee. Here, it's always at your fingertips."
(Alar Hirv, a barista who moved to Viljandi)

For most of our post-marital lives, the Chef and I have enjoyed a certain ritual. He drops the children off at school at about 8 am, and then arrives at my one-bedroom apartment in the Posti Street house for our first coffee or *fika*. I always used a Swedish blend, and he instructs me on the finer points of managing one's coffee, such as that it has to be refrigerated at all times, or it will go bad, and sometimes I turn around and find my coffee has already been returned to the refrigerator without me noticing it, this time with a rubber band around it to keep it fresh. If I don't show the coffee the same amount of respect that he does, there's a high level of "tsk, tsk," or his eyes will even bulge, and he will grimace.

"What? What the hell are you doing to your coffee?"

He never expresses such concern about people, you know. People are on their own. People do their own things, and if something bad happens to them, that's their own business. "The difference between people and coffee," he says, "is that coffee is innocent." For the Chef, coffee demands a certain amount of respect, the way you might treat a religious icon.

"I'm sorry, I'm so sorry," I'll say whenever something goes wrong.

"My God, man, don't let it happen again!"

"It will never happen again. I promise, I promise!"

I have a good moka espresso maker for the first fika, which is consumed sometimes with a bit of almond milk or cream, depending on whatever I have on hand. His stories are the usual and the similar: divorce, family logistics, financial issues. We talk about women, though not too much, and sometimes I worry we might be into the same ones, but just not talking about it.

Viljandi is a small town, after all. Such a small town. He dreams of setting up a podcast where we will get thousands in advertising money just to talk about gruff Estonian woodsmen and taskmaster Estonian women. We'll do it in Estonian with our goofy accents and the show will be called "*Kuradi valismaalased!*" or, "Those Damn Foreigners!" We take promotional photos outside my barn, with each of us holding up armfuls of firewood. But we don't get far.

After the first *fika*, we go to the cafe for the second *fika*. This is enjoyed together with the cafe club, *kohvikuklubi*, which consists of me, the Chef, Jõeste, and Musi, a mysterious, dark-haired woman who always wears a scarf on her head. Musi is a bit older than us, a managerial type, and speaks with authority on all matters, often dangling a manicured finger before her. She is convinced that what I need most in life is another woman and even advises me from time to time on which type would be most suitable for me. When I tell her I'm not that interested, she just waves that finger. "Time, time," she will say. "You need more time!"

Occasionally, Heldi, an event planner from Järvamaa, will join us and similarly advise me. We almost universally have the macchiato at the café. Although honestly, I think Heldi prefers the latte. Jõeste always has two macchiatos and always in quick succession. Then she will grumble about how her doctor told her she needs to cut back on coffee, and that in the future she might only be able to have one macchiato, or maybe just an espresso. The horror! All kinds of things go on at *kohvikuklubi*. All kinds of adult things go on. Sometimes one of Jõeste's former lovers comes into the cafe and she'll be forced to speak with him. Sometimes Miss Cloud traipses through in a fog and then Jõeste elbows me in the ribs. All kinds of other things are going on, too.

Things that I don't even know about yet.

Jõeste and I have developed our own special rapport. We are members of *kohvikuklubi*, but we have our own mini *kohvikuklubi*. Jõeste is two years older than me, so whenever I sit with her, I feel a little anxious, the way a boy might feel when he sits with an older girl at school. What I really love to do is tease Jõeste with romantic overtures. I come up Koidu Street and see her head behind the window glass, blow a patch of fog on the window, and draw a heart in the middle with my finger. Then Jõeste laughs and maybe blushes, blowing me a kiss.

"Well," she says each morning, "what news today? *Mis uudis on?*"

This is the codeword for what is going on with various female characters in my life. Together, Jõeste and I assemble a list of potential love interests with nicknames. For the fun of it, we add each other's names to the list. Jõeste's nickname is the *kuduja*, or knitter. She is actually well-known in the world of Estonian knitting and does a brisk trade in handmade gloves. People from the US sometimes arrive in Viljandi and seek her out, and then she is obliged to entertain them. Jõeste doesn't always relish this attention. It's not just speaking in English; it's having to be friendly and sociable that annoys our poor Jõeste. She runs to the cafe to get another macchiato and decompresses.

Jõeste is a taciturn Estonian lady, you see. She answers questions with one word. *"Hästi," "Niisama,"* or sometimes two. *"Mul ükskõik."* She likes music and then disappears into her headphones. She loves electronic music the most. Sometimes Jõeste DJs at the Airplane Factory, the *Lennukitehas,* at 2 AM. This really is a former factory where they once made airplanes in the 1920s and then buses thereafter. We all have to go there and wait until we're half asleep and she comes out and blasts Depeche Mode and Gary Numan songs. Sometimes I really do crawl on top of the ping-pong table and sleep as she plays.

But she has an active social life. Jõeste has emerged from her marriage on a singular mission to find a partner. This is what she wants. Men drift into and out of her life, and she sees it as an experiment in finding the right fit.

"Alati võiks proovida," she says and chuckles. "One can always try!"

She scolds me for not dating anyone.

"I've already had five," she says. "And you've had how many? None?"

"What about Miss Cloud?"

"Don't waste your time. She's a young fool. They all are."

"What do you mean by all of them?"

"All these young girls expect to be treated like princesses. They are burning themselves out traveling around the world looking for Mr. Right. So let her go and find him. Let her keep searching."

"Is that how it ends? When they meet Mr. Right?"

"No," she sips from her cup. "It ends when they have children. Then harsh reality sets in. Then they are somebody's mother. They can't be princesses anymore." She chuckles to herself. Our wise Jõeste. She doesn't expect to be treated like a princess, but she is searching too.

Though it seems that I am destined to remain alone here. Even the Chef has found someone new.

It happens one morning that the Chef just doesn't show up for his morning *fika*. I have the moka boiling, and that good black gold is shooting out, like I had just struck oil. The sting of coffee aroma hangs in the air, and I've taken the almond milk out, set out the two small cups on the table, and have a few slices of rubbery, but still good, halloumi cheese on a plate. The first *fika* is set, but at 8:05 AM, there is still no Chef. And then again at 8:30 AM, there is still no Chef. At last, I'm forced to call him, mostly out of fear that he will arrive and the coffee might be too hot, or too cold. He's a finicky Swede, if you know what I mean. Particular in his tastes. At last, I get a hold of this elusive cook on the phone, but I can't say it's much of a conversation.

"Where are you? The coffee is ready. I've been waiting for half an hour!"

"What? Oh ..." There's some crackling noise in the background, like the wind, and then I hear what sounds like a woman's voice in the distance. Then that odd noise again.

"So, are you coming?"

"What?"

"Are you coming for the first fika? Or should we meet at the cafe?"

"Huh?"

"Do you want me to wait for you?"

"What?" That strange crackling noise again.

"Damn it, man, where the hell are you?"

"I'm ... I just can't talk right now. Something's come up. I'm on the other side of town."

For some reason, I'm the last to find out what happened. Yet it seems everyone else knows. Jõeste knows, and when we have our weekly sauna meeting at the Chef's place, Pepi the Argentinian comes and he also knows.

"So, you two have known each other for a long time?" he asks in Estonian, but in his clipped Argentinian accent. "How do you feel about it? Are you sure it's love?"

"*Targad ei torma*," said the Chef, sweating. "Fools don't rush in. I need to think about it."

Feel about what? Think about what?

I ask him, but he refuses to tell me.

"I need to think some more. Mull things over. We've been friends for so long."

Who is it then? Is it the Designer? Or is it even Miss Cloud? The thought of it being either of them depresses me. Even the Chef notices my sour mood.

"What's the matter with you?" he asks. "Cold ate out your heart?"

"Something like that."

"You're a real moody bastard, you know that? Just take some more maca."

Then one morning at our cafe club, I notice that Musi and the Chef are sitting together. They are sitting very close to each other, leaning over the table in each other's faces. The Chef says something and Musi laughs as if it's the funniest thing she has ever heard.

"Now do you see what has happened?" whispers Jõeste in my ear.

That's how it goes with us men. One day your friend is there for *fika*, and the next day he isn't around anymore. He's somewhere else with someone else. Somewhere far off on the other side of town. All for that thing they call love.

Now in the mornings, I am making the first *fika* alone, with my little moka gurgling away, with the rain and mist outside. And I start to wonder if I will be next.

LITTLE BEE GLUE

"When a man has the right woman, he does everything at the right time."
(A.H. Tammsaare (1878–1940), "I Loved a German", 1935)

That autumn, Miss Cloud comes to work at the cafe, and at last I feel inspired to write again. She does not come to stay, however, for the exotic woman named Cloud actually has no home. She's now a wanderer, a hobo. Still, some people, including Jõeste at the cafe, will admit that Miss Cloud is *arukas*, or wise. She lives by her wits, goes with the wind. At the same time, she is shiftless and transient. She lives out of suitcases and bags, many stuffed with her worldly possessions. Sometimes she drags a suitcase behind her, but usually it's just a backpack.

In Viljandi, she's sleeping at the confectioner's residence in Orika, a little village beyond the lake. Here she makes fires at night and reads *The Heart of the Bear* by firelight before dozing off into sweet, sweaty snores. During the daytime, she works under the watchful eye of Kaari making gingerbread.

I study her when she works at the cafe. I watch her stumble through the doorways with lattes and platters of *pada*. When she serves customers, she smiles and says, *Ole lahke*. Be kind!

"*Ole ise lahke,*" I respond. "Be kind yourself."

"It's just a phrase you say," she squints. "You're reading too much into things, again."

"What do you mean, 'again'?"

"Now, now. Be kind," she grins.

"Whatever," I grumble and type away. "I'll try to be kinder to you."

"*Tubli.*"

After that, all of the servers at the cafe start telling me to be kind. This is how Miss Cloud continues to play her tricks on me. Yet I also love to be tricked by her. Sometimes, if she walks by, she will whisper something in my ear, or give me a tickle, but otherwise continues on nonchalantly, as if nothing happened. I write her love letters. Lots of love letters. But she cannot be bothered to respond. She yawns with her voluminous book, beside the fire. Then she sleeps.

I hate her with the white heat of a thousand hydrogen bombs. I hate how she toys with me. Yet it's also true that I admire her. There's just something about girls who live out of bags.

"You should tell her," the Chef advises me. "Just go up to her one day and say, 'You're the one.'"

I can't do that though. Miss Cloud will laugh in my face.

Sometimes on the weekends Miss Cloud returns to her parents' farm on the north coast where she gathers with her many siblings, whose names I can never recall. One is a scientist; another is a guitarist. There are other Clouds too. In fact, the whole village is overrun with Clouds. The mayor is a Cloud, I imagine, as is the postman. The fishermen are too. They call out to each other from neighboring orchards. If you need some flour or an egg, you borrow it from the others. Miss Cloud has grown up by the sea, but is afraid to venture there alone in the dark.

"I'm afraid there might be murderers in the forests," she has confided in me. "*Metsamõrvarid.*"

Then one night she went to a party in Tallinn and came home very upset because someone told her she didn't look like a real Estonian with her cocoa skin and Ingrian looks. "How can it be? I'm Estonian and they think they have the right to tell me I don't look like one?"

"Because people always expect Estonians to look like the blonde girls on the chocolate boxes," I said. "And you don't look anything like a girl who sells chocolate."

She will only go with one of her sisters down to the coastline to collect shells in summer, she has told me. In the winter, when the Cloud family gathers, they go sledding. At night she is with her dogs who are separated by a door so that they don't make more dogs. "It's awfully sad," she will lament. "They so desire to be together."

These are her secrets, the secrets she keeps from me, as we drift into the Christmas season, with her rising early and making buckwheat gingerbreads in the back with Kaari, the enticing aroma trailing her apron everywhere. I just kept writing silently, with my head down. No amount of words, late-night ramblings, emotional outpours could touch this person's windy heart.

Only once in a while will she talk to me in public. Most days I am ignored. Although I do catch Miss Cloud watching me. I catch her watching me as she brings out soup, or ginger-bread.

Then I look down and ignore her back. "Be kind yourself," I whisper. "*Ole ise siis lahke.*"

Then one day, she comes and sits with me, as if she has been planning to all the time. We go to the back of the house behind the cafe. It is dark and we sit on the couch by the iron furnace and put our legs up on the burlap sacks of coffee. It is gentle and warm back in there, with our bodies side by side, and that strong aroma of hot coffee roast. She weaves yarn with her fingers back and forth and I watch the spider rhythm of her hands, the flecks of gingerbread dough still on her skin.

"Isn't this place wonderful?" she whispers to me. "It looks just like a time-ship here."

"A time-ship?"

"That's what I call it. An *ajalaev*. All we need to do is sit and we could go back in time."

We are very still and sit there waiting. One can only hear the fire.

"You know," she says, weaving. "I really do want a man to love me. But men are so untrustworthy. They say they love you, but this love doesn't mean much. You can't believe it. You can't trust them."

"You don't have to trust me," I say.

"Oh really?"

"Yes. But I could love you as well. If you let me."

She eyes me with suspicion, then says, "But you have lived your life. *Sul on elatud elu.*"

"Because I have been married and have children?"

She nods.

I give her a kiss. This catches her by surprise, but there is a lot of truth in it. "That is true," I say. "I have lived my life, just as you say, but that doesn't mean that I cannot love you."

We sit there a bit longer beside the fire. "Just take it for what it is," I tell her. "Nothing more." She tinkers with her knitting. I finally let out the big love-feeling that has been building up in my chest, unwrap it slowly, all without a word. I let the love-feeling flow between us in total silence. The air is thick and rubbery with it.

"There," I say. "See, nothing has changed."

She looks up at me as if she is a bit drunk and says, "Maybe you should hang out with Enn more. Learn to build me a time-ship. An *ajalaev.*"

The door swings open and we see Enn's face peering back at us in the darkness. Then he begins to sing us a song. It sounds like an old dreamy love song, something by Frank Sinatra.

Miss Cloud puts her hand to her mouth and squeals. I grip the couch as if I was on a ride. Why is he singing? Then he tips his hat to us with a wink, shuts the door with a bang, and vanishes into the night. We both burst into laughter. Who knew Enn liked Frank Sinatra?

I decide then that I will do something sweet for her, but I don't know what to do. "You should get her something that reminds you of her," the Chef recommends. Even though he is younger, he seems to have more of a natural finesse for these kinds of things. "Get her something sweet."

The sweetest thing I can think of is to buy her some honey. But what kind? There are so many types. At the Christmas Fair at Sakala Keskus, I search the mounds of arts and crafts and sausages for the sweet stuff. I acquire one jar, then another and put it in my pocket. Then I come upon a tub of the most delicious cream marked as *taruvaik* or "bee glue". It is honey mixed with a substance bees make from evergreens and other needle-leaved trees. To taste it is to taste a pine forest. This alone will do for her, along with all the honey I can fit in my pockets.

Then, a few mornings later, I summon my courage and strength. That morning at the cafe, the Chef's new girlfriend Musi helps me prepare the gift, stacking the honey jars, wrapping them, and then attaching little bells to the ribbons. She is so pleased to encourage me on my romantic adventure, but I refuse to divulge the name of the woman who has earned my love and respect. There is also a box of turmeric powder for making turmeric lattes, *kuldnepiim*, "golden milk," Miss Cloud's favorite drink.

I fear the worst as Musi wraps the gift. A merciless assassination of my heart. I am waiting to be ridiculed, crushed, made fun of, shattered to smithereens, toyed with, and turned into the laughing-stock of the cafe. There is just a sliver of orange December sunlight on the horizon when I set off for the *Lossi Kommuun,* where she is now living. The cold streets are dense with shadows and tufts of chimney smoke. When I at last reach the house, I go inside.

It's my first time in the *Kommuun,* which is on the second floor of Lossi 7, a big yellow villa, the so-called *Kirsimäe Maja,* or "Cherry Hill House." It's my first time that I have seen the commune's worn, weathered couches and kitchen utensils, the beaten-up old floorboards, its cats that sit in the corners who belong to someone. This is how so many of Viljandi's women live. Women like Miss Cloud. Waitresses and hairstylists, who work unsteady jobs, making a pittance but still getting by, dreaming of saving up enough to go somewhere else for a while.

They are survivors, yet theirs is a sisterhood. They sleep in the same beds, drink from the same cups, wash themselves in the same showers. At night, they decorate each other's hands with henna. No matter how destitute or impoverished, they retain their softness of heart.

When I arrive, Miss Cloud's thick hair is pulled up and she wears a sky-blue sweater and she looks more like a little girl than a grandmother. She watches me with tired eyes – she has just woken up. I very hesitantly inform her that I have a gift for her, and hand it over.

She receives the package in a queenly manner, as if it was all expected. Miss Cloud takes the gifts out and appreciates each one, yawning between words of thanks, but she likes the bell from the ribbon the most, and shakes it close to her ear, just to hear its tiny Christmas jingly ring.

"This may be the greatest Christmas gift anyone has ever given me," she says.

She also likes the *taruvaik* honey, its tree sap taste, and we let it seep into cups of tea.

"Thank you," she says. "*Taruvaik* is actually my favorite."

After that, I start to call her *taruvaiguke*. "Little Bee Glue."

As the first winter snows begin to fall beyond the windows, I have to wonder, could it be that my years of lonesomeness are drawing to an end? Would we soon be as cozy as the Chef and his Musi? Would it all end like Enn had once said? "Wait until the right girl sets her eye on you."

RESTLESS SOULS

"Oh, gigantic paradox, too utterly monstrous for solution!"
(Edgar Allen Poe (1809–1849), "William Wilson," 1839)

There are certain details that catch your attention when you're in Romaan at 4 AM. The tiny ceramic statue of Confucius on the counter, for example, or the poster of the Beach Boys on the wall. "That's Dennis Wilson," I tell the Designer. "He's the drummer who drowned. And that's Mike Love over there. He's the Beach Boy who sued everybody else later."

Then I turn around and see that I am talking to myself.

There's a frothy December moisture on the windows, an old lamp, and a table where a young couple are seated playing cards. It's an Estonian deck, with paintings by Konrad Mägi and Eduard Viiralt on the backs of the cards. But the young woman is a Russian dancer in a puffy jacket. She looks like an extra from a hip-hop video. Linnuse Artur, the bearded *karmoška* player from Zetod, is at the bar. Romaan will be open until 5 AM, he informs the restless crowd, but no later.

There is a collective groan. "Not fair!" someone shouts. Linnus just nods in a kind, paternal way. *"Nii on.* That's just how it is." It is one of the few times I have heard Mr. Linnus speak at all. Usually, he just stands there with a dreamy look on his face.

I leave the small back room at the bar, descend the steps into the main room of Romaan, where a small crowd has gathered. At the center of this crowd stands the Designer, her golden locks sticking out from under a blue cap, goopy makeup dripping from her eyes. The evening had started innocently enough at Fellin's birthday party. Yet that was hours ago and somehow the night refuses to die. Miss Cloud lies on a couch in a stupor. She watches the scene wearily. She yawns, then glances at the lines in the ceiling. It's as if her insides have been vacuumed out.

Yet the Designer does not give up so easily. She's telling everyone she's leaving Estonia. "We were fired from our job in Tallinn," she says. "And I'm bored here! Bored! Bored! Bored!"

This is not exactly true. First of all, she has a fine job as a teacher in Tallinn. It was a part-time gig at some esoteric shop they were fired from, and yes, the Designer and Miss Cloud received word that night that they had been relieved of their duties and with good reason, I think, because they are two of the most obnoxious, caustic, ragged, restless people I know when they are together. Together they like to sing old Michael Jackson songs, and not even his better material. Singing the theme song to *Free Willy* in public is bound to get you fired.

"Bored, bored, bored!" she goes on. The people around her are riveted. The Designer is usually a cool cookie, but now she is having a real moment. "I'm soooo bored!" Then her eyes meet mine while I stand on the stairs, and there is a wet tear in them. "Signore Justin Petrone!" she cries aloud. "Take me to Italy with you! We leave immediately! And make sure to bring lots of money!"

"I don't have any money," I say. "And I think it's time we go home now." I come down the steps and try to take her by the arm, but she pulls away from me.

"Not yet! Isn't there some place that's open? Someplace we can get some food?"

"It's four o'clock in the morning!"

"So what? Don't you understand how bored I am here, Petrone? We're stuck in Viljandi. We could be in Barcelona! Or Rome! Let's all leave!"

"Just come home with me. I'll make some *tatrapuder*. Buckwheat porridge."

"I don't want any of your damn *tatrapuder*!"

"Please come home. You need to sleep."

"No! I am not going anywhere," she says. "Now, where was I? Oh, yes. We were fired in Tallinn. *Meid vallandati!*"

DJ Jaanika shows up in the middle of this and orders a beer. Miss Cloud is still stretched out on the couch, but it might as well be a hospital ward stretcher. She fills up the couch with her dark coat and hair. I keep looking at her, but she is immune to my needy glances. All she needs now is that last shot, the *coup de grace*, to finish her off and she'll be deep asleep.

"Jaanika!" The Designer seizes the young DJs arm and the DJ's hoop earrings dangle. "We were laid off in Tallinn and I am just so bored here! Bored, bored, bored! It's time to leave."

"That's not true," I interject. "You are not telling the truth. You have other jobs. You're a teacher. Miss Cloud makes gingerbread cookies."

"Nobody asked you!"

"I heard you were moving to Spain anyway," says DJ Jaanika, and takes a sip of her beer.

"Petrone, you told everyone I was moving to Spain!" the Designer cocks an eye at me.

"Rome. I definitely told them Rome."

"You said Spain! You told everyone in Viljandi I was moving and I told you not to tell!"

"Maybe you told someone else about Spain. It wasn't me."

"Pwah! That never happened!"

I'm too tired to follow the rest of the conversation. Something about going on Tinder and finding a sugar daddy. Someone who can take them out of Viljandi. She wants more than this. More, more, more!

"Don't you get it," I say. "Everywhere is nowhere. There's no difference where you go."

"Yes! Yes, there is a difference! Some places have beaches and palm trees. And it's warm there!" Her energy is electric. Her eyes are full of wired tension. This is not the subdued girl who reappeared on my 38th birthday as if nothing had happened and we were all still just friends. This is not the girl who sketches quietly and reads books about angels. At last, the Designer goes to leave, but she drops her gloves on the floor and yet doesn't even go to pick them up. She just leaves them there at the foot of the couch. She can't even be bothered. Then I pick them up and help her put them on, finger by finger. "Aren't these the ones you bought at Sõbralt Sõbrale?"

"Yes, they are, in fact. And they only cost two euros!"

"Two euros?" whistles DJ Jaanika. "What a deal!"

"These boots? I got them there too. They were also cheap. These socks were 50 cents!"

After the Designer exits the door of Romaan, I think she is done. "But I don't want to go home," she says, as we head into the streets. "No! I'm bored, I tell you. Bored, bored, bored! Let's go get some fries!"

At about six o'clock in the morning, we roll home in the dark. I give the Designer my bed on the pull-out couch, pull all the camping mattresses out and assemble them on the floor for me and Cloud. These young women have been the constant in my life now for more than a year. My heart undulates between them. Yet I cannot say what any of it means anymore, if I love one more than the other, or in a different kind of way. Are they both my friends? Are they both my secret loves? I just can't say anymore. All I know is that they are here, sleeping together in my room.

In the backroom, my daughter sits up briefly and eyes the scene with tired eyes, then tries to go back to sleep. I had put her to sleep before slipping out the door for the party at Fellin down the street hours ago. Somehow, I don't feel like anything is out of the ordinary about coming home with two women at six o'clock in the morning to a one-bedroom apartment.

Normaalne, as they say. Later, as they slumber at last, my daughter whispers questions to me through the dark.

"But what time did you come home, Dad?"

"At two am," I say.

"That's not true. You came home at six. I checked."

"That's true then. It must have been six."

"But how old is Miss Cloud?" she asks.

"She's 28."

"And the Designer?"

"She turned 30 in May."

"Oh. Thirty then." Maybe it sounds ancient to a 10-year-old. She yawns and snuggles in her bed and drifts back to sleep. To me, they are still kids even if by every metric they are mature young women. I'm 38 and have been through some things at this point. A lot of things, actually.

Everyone sleeps then, and outside the temperature has dropped and all is ice. I even had to carry the Designer on my back for a while, so she wouldn't slip, though she insisted that she was perfectly capable of walking on the ice and was just too lazy to walk at 5 AM. That was on the way to Vanalinna Burger, where Miss Cloud decided to steal one of the toy elves in the Christmas window display before running out into the street, the Designer behind her. The innocent little toy elf now hangs suspended from the window like some trophy of war.

"Thanks for the elf," I whisper to Miss Cloud. "I shall cherish it always and think of you."

"Please be quiet. I'm trying to sleep!"

Then I give her a kiss on the cheek and she blushes a bit but pulls her blankets tighter to her face. I turn over again with my back to her. "Enjoy that kiss. It's the last one you'll ever get."

"*Kuidas soovid*," she yawns. "As you wish."

Later, the Designer awakes with the most splendid headache. She requests that I go to the cafe at once to see if Musi has an aspirin, which I do. Musi comes through, and soon I am back with a little pill and a glass of water. She gulps it down, blinks her eyes, and looks up at me.

"Seriously," she whispers. "I'm so bored here, Signore Petrone. Please take me to Italy."

"Not right now," I say. "Maybe someday."

Miss Cloud gets up and crawls into bed beside her friend. The two of them snuggle and look at me as I watch them. The Designer places both arms around her good friend and gives her a loving squeeze. Miss Cloud squints up at me with her lush and fleshy face. I feel *so* confused.

"*Härra* Petrone," says the Designer. "Did you ever imagine we'd both be in your bed?"

I say nothing but my blush only makes them laugh more. Then I go to make them coffee.

That's the day when they cook sweet potatoes and squash while singing folk songs together as they cook. They sing folk songs about knitting, and even sit quietly knitting for a while in our home. For once, we have a beautiful feeling of having women in our house. Women who cook. Women who sing songs. Women who are obnoxious but still love you deeply.

But they are so bored that their restless souls can't keep them in Viljandi.

Later that afternoon, they take a van back to Tallinn in search of adventures. But before they leave, I give the Designer, this young woman who has once broken my heart and inspired me to burn my journal on an already prehistoric and evil St. John's Day, a loving, warm embrace. Then I turn to face Miss Cloud. She will not be returning to Viljandi anymore, she says, and even if she does, then only to visit.

I push her hair away from her face and say, "Goodbye *taruvaiguke*" and kiss her head.

They climb into the van and speed away. Within minutes, they are gone. After that, Miss Cloud goes to her parents' farm for a while, then returns to Tallinn, where she sleeps on the floor next to the Designer's bed. She writes to me sometimes and tells me about how sad, restless, and bored she is, and sometimes she just flees parties so she can be alone.

Then, some weeks later, Miss Cloud moves away to Iceland. She never tells me. It's the Designer who breaks the news to me one evening when she comes to visit me in Viljandi. When she does, I feel a fissure within open up, as if all the ice has shattered below. This is not sadness. More a feeling of resignation. Sometimes I wonder why I even bother trying at all, but such has become the nature of this life. I go back to the cafe with my journal. With my projects. That's all.

Miss Cloud does send me one last photo. It's of her on that faraway jagged coastline with a girlish grin, a patch of sunlight on her face, hair tousled, eating two dripping cones of pink raspberry ice cream with my gray beloved Atlantic Ocean behind her, drifting away and away.

At the photo shop on Tartu Street, I have them print out the image of the enigmatic girl and slip it into the last page of my journal. Then I close the book and put it away in a drawer.

THE POSTI STREET COMMUNE

"I have a good opinion of Viljandi. It's small, nice, beau-
tiful, and cozy, but still a very culturally vibrant town.
Now, if you will excuse me, I have to run!"
(Villu Talsi, a musician who has lived in Viljandi, and
often has to run to rehearsals.)

A long time ago, when the Chef was still married and he
shared his home with his wife and children on Mäe Street,
while I shared my home with my wife and children on Sepa
Street, there was a day when my whole family was away and
I decided that I would like nothing more than to take a quiet
bath. We had a wonderful wooden bathtub, a *tunnivann*, and
I would fill it to the brim with hot water and just get in and
soak.

It so happened that day that the Chef decided to pop by
unannounced. This was not out of the ordinary. What was out
of the ordinary was that I was naked in a bathtub.

"Juss?" he called out to me. "Jussike? Are you home?"

I didn't answer.

"Jussike? *Halloo?*"

I thought by staying quiet he would think that no one
was at home. Instead, he came in the unlocked front door –
because nobody locks their doors in Viljandi – and started
searching for me around the house.

"Juss? Jussike? Where are you anyway? I know you're here somewhere."

I only lowered myself deeper into the tub as I heard his footsteps grow louder.

"*Juss?*"

No answer. I now had only my nose and mouth above the water line, so that I could breathe. I thought of war movies I had seen, where soldiers hid themselves underwater like that. The next thing I knew, he was at the bathroom door. He opened it and called into the room. "*Juss?*" Then, to my relief, he closed the door and left the house, but not before using my toilet.

When I finally heard his footsteps pass under the window outside, I at last pulled myself out of the tub water and exhaled. That was a real Viljandi moment, you know. That was a close call. Sometimes this whole town is like one big student dormitory.

The Chef hasn't changed, by the way. This winter it's the same, because he's the Chef, and he just has a different understanding of people and borders. He's not rude, he just has a different concept of what might be appropriate in any given moment. It's not unusual for the Chef, for instance, to come into your apartment at midnight, creep into your bedroom, and stand by your bed.

"*Hey, are you sleeping?*" the Chef asks looking down.

"Actually, I was," I say, pulling the blanket to my nose.

"Oh," he steps back. "I was just going to have a drink. And we have some leftover soup."

"What kind of soup?"

"Lentil soup. With loads of garlic."

"Well, okay, I suppose so."

This is how I wind up getting out of bed at midnight for a snack with the Chef, my new neighbor. At the end of the old year, he gave up his beachside apartment with the wonderful ceiling, and started subletting my one-room bedroom apartment. "It's just temporary," he promised me. "All temporary. At least until I get back on my feet!"

I moved into a larger, newly renovated apartment across the hall. This one had a large bedroom in the back and a smaller one for my daughter. There was also a living room and a kitchen, a toilet and a shower. The plumbing mostly worked, the oven was new, and none of the neighbors were drunks. All of these things felt like real luxuries in the Old Town.

This is our own commune here, the Posti Street Commune. Kristina is next door with her Italian boyfriend, Alessandro. There's General Ly, the yoga instructor upstairs, and Kadri, the school director next door with Volli, the little white dog she shares with her ex-husband, so that half the time, the dog is with him and half the time it is with her. Then Jüri the Singer comes along to do *remont* on the apartment he owns across the yard. We were and are all one big family here at Posti Street. One big happy Viljandi family.

The Chef stays in the small apartment in between stints as a cook in Oslo, where he hangs out with other Scandinavian chefs, one of whom at least has a blow-up doll in his

139

apartment, or so I have heard. A few others are coke addicts, I think. "I saw one in the back, snorting it off a key," he said. People in the culinary trade, as I have come to learn, are a different sort. They're hedonistic, a bit shameless, but in a heartwarming, dopey way. They mean no harm, they just enjoy sex, drugs sometimes, and a finely-done *demi-glace*. A chef will do suspicious things and think nothing of it. A chef will rob an ice cream truck and then explain it away by saying, "Well, the door was open anyway." Or he'll tiptoe into your bedroom at midnight, wake you up, and ask you if you want some lentil soup.

When the Chef is really tired, he just goes to sleep. The time of day is no factor in this. The Chef will just yawn and say, "I'm tired and I am going to sleep now." Then he lies on top of his bedsheets and sleeps. Just like that. Even at 2 PM in the afternoon, he'll sleep. When I go in, I discover the half-clothed man with long hair is silent, as if meditating.

He looks like the Buddha, I think. He's a Chef Buddha.

I've loaned the Chef a copy of Anthony Bourdain's memoir, *Kitchen Confidential*. He loves it. He is studying Bourdain in the meantime as his lentil soup simmers on the stove with loads of garlic. He is learning. The book lies across his chest as he slumbers in the afternoons. He is reading about how Bourdain liked to steal chefs from other kitchens for his restaurants.

Bourdain is also a kind of idol to him now. Chef Buddha Bourdain.

When the Chef is in Viljandi, his three children come and stay with him. Sometimes Musi, the Chef's girlfriend, comes to visit us and brings her son, too. And sometimes my youngest daughter surfaces from Põlvamaa, where her mother is now living. Then the Designer comes and stays because she's teaching classes at the Academy now and then. The population of our commune is therefore four adults and six children. Clothing is shared, exchanged. Socks from one apartment wind up in the other. Once, I even found a green dress that no one could account for. The origin of the green dress baffled us for weeks. Musi swore it didn't belong to her. It didn't fit our daughters. Much later, I found out who owned the dress, but I was sworn to secrecy about its provenance. At least some things must remain secret in Viljandi. Only some things.

Meals are consumed collectively. The Chef whips up soups and pasta dishes and the children eat together around the table with assorted bowls and spoons. The Designer remarks that we have now become a *kargpere*, a mixed family. She lies on my couch with her golden hair curls flowing. She is so tired because she works seven days a week, crisscrossing the country to give lessons on upcycling and the like. Turning old trash into something new. Her students adore her. Yet the workload is breaking our superwoman. She is still a taciturn type, one of these Estonian girls from out in the marshes who never complains. Most of her family are still out there, deep in the woods. Her grandfather is a fur trapper and makes vests out of beaver pelts.

I spill my heart out to her, and all she can say through tired lips is *"noh jah,"* or *"jah, nii ongi, jah."* I really love her still, and would carry her bags and fetch any items for her whenever she wants, no matter the size. She asks for a drill and I give one to her lovingly. Miss Cloud? She broke my heart and ran off to Iceland, or Greenland, or wherever. But the Designer? She is still here! Always, mysteriously here! With my tool in her hand, this strange character drills a few holes in a piece of wood and then vanishes.

There is a cold winter wind howling all around. She doesn't even explain what it's for, only mumbles it has something to do with the Academy. Watching the Designer come and go, I've started to ponder that maybe I could do well with a woman just like this, a woman who is *asjalik*, practical, who doesn't run away, who knows what she needs, and when she wants it, and how. Not her, as I understand it, but someone like her then. If you're going to serve somebody, it might as well be someone who knows what she is doing.

APRIL STORM

"And there received him three queens with great mourning; and so, they set them down, and in one of their laps King Arthur laid his head."
(Thomas Malory (1415–1471), "Le Morte D'Arthur", 1485.)

Spring again, allegedly. I arrive at the cafe for a good macchiato, where I encounter Simon, that poor lost sound engineer and musician, sitting by the window and staring at the wet flakes of snow as they drift down. Simon, who used to be so happy with his Duran Duran and friends at Mulks. Simon, who swore he would never take a sauna because it was too gay.

Yet something has happened to Simon in the interim. He looks as if he has gone mad.

Down, down the snow drifts outside, and Simon the engineer, who was only supposed to stay for RetroFest, watches the snow fall, brooding beneath his black hair in the corner like Professor Snape at Hogwarts. The empty tundra reality of Viljandi is dawning on him, I think, dragging him down with all the snow. Where there once was a jovial musician is now a shadow of a man shoveling porridge into his mouth mindlessly, taking a sip of his coffee and then his tea, his coffee and then his tea. He alternates between mumbling, eating, and sipping. Mumbling, eating, and sipping. He drops spoonfuls of sugar into his coffee. So much sugar. Soon the cup will be full of sugar. That familiar dead-fish gaze. I'm starting to worry about Simon's mental health.

"So, Simon, how are you?" I say, taking a seat beside the shaky man.

"It's April 1st," our Simon mutters back. "It's April 1st and there's a bloody snowstorm."

There is something off about his blue eyes. Is it winter madness? Cabin fever? Something just isn't right. It's that hundred-yard stare. Some veterans of foreign wars have it.

"April 1st," Simon continues mumbling to himself. "It's April 1st! It should be 15 degrees outside, but it's not. It's the same old shit, mate. Every day here in V. is just the same old shit."

I am starting to worry about Simon the sound engineer. I worry about him because I too was once a novice foreigner living in Viljandi. I know what it can do to you, bring out the darker aspects of one's psyche. To others, it's all just some gay ball, the lights and the costumes, the dizzying patterns of the bagpipes and fiddles, the *kodutaika*, where the ladies get together to sell and buy clothes at different people's homes, the Ugala Theatre applause. In the autumn, at the Ait they have the *Lõikuspidu*, the Harvest Party, and the winners get a wooden ladle, an *etnokulp*, as a prize. That's how it looks from the outside. Cute and normal. *Kena ja normaalne.*

Yet, if you mix in all of those haunted ruined houses, such as the old laundry on Tartu Street, which has been collapsing for centuries it seems, with the sense of isolation you can get living here, and that gray that just never seems to leave, so that you forget there even is a sun, then madness might be lurking around the corner, ready to follow you home like a Viljandi cat.

At Layk Cafe on Turu Street the next day, I see Simon again, who is still zombied from the weather. Yet even in distress, he retains the genteel manners of the Englishman. He's still staring out the window, muttering dark oaths under his breath so no one can hear him. Without the inexplicable allure of Estonian womanhood, he would be on tour with some band. Simple enough. Yet now he's living in some flat by the marketplace with his brood. He stares out the windows there too, cursing. These days when he's not in the Green House Cafe cursing, he's at Layk amusing himself. He marches in like an old headmaster and takes a seat by the window.

"What bloody language are they speaking in here anyway?" he grumbles bitterly. "*Hungarian*?"

"Estonian," I say from a nearby table. "You are in Estonia now, Simon. You know that."

"Same difference."

Simon has been down on Viljandi since the day a few local Nazis saluted him. He seems to be a magnet for Nazis, and will pull out his phone and show you the photos of these characters with their red swastika armbands who tend to appear when he is around. He imagines there are Nazi sleeper cells around every corner in town, and ponders that some of the well-known cultural figures and businessmen in town might also have Hitlerite sympathies. At night they are meeting in the basements of private clubs and synchronizing their German-made wrist watches. His concerns are well founded though. One line of Simon's family were Lithuanian Jews. He knows the local Jewish history. He knows that a section of Pikk Street in Viljandi was once called Jew Street and there was a vibrant Jewish community here before the Germans came.

"And if you ask anyone where they went, they'll just shrug their shoulders," Simon says. "'We didn't have anything to do with it.' If you didn't have anything to do with it, then who did?" One day, we even take a drive out to Vana-Võidu on the edge of town to visit the old Jewish cemetery, which has a memorial to all the local families cut down by the fascists in 1941, and beautiful old stones inscribed in Hebrew. Here lie Viljandiers with names like Shapiro and Bloch. And there are stones placed on the memorials, because there still are Jews living in Viljandi. At least some survived.

Simon places stones on the tombs out of respect. He photographs swastikas painted on the rubbish bins by the kindergartens, notes the "Sons of Odin" types who wear black sweatshirts that show a gallow with nooses hanging from each end. I've seen these types as well, but I don't know what to do about them. They used to trouble me too. It used to enrage me to see someone with a Waffen SS t-shirt at the supermarket. In Viljandi though, it has all somehow become *normaalne*. I just ignore it, like I ignore the drunks in the park, like I ignore the racist graffiti, like I ignore the broken sidewalks. I feel as if I should be Simon's guardian angel here. "Take it easy, mate. Take it all as it comes." I'm failing. Simon doesn't know what the word *tubli* means. He thinks people are saying *tupla* which is a chocolate bar.

Today, Simon finds solace in spending time with his little twin girls, who sit munching on some potatoes, as well as strolling by the lake. Just then, a Duran Duran song comes on the playlist at Layk. "Did I ever tell you I partied with Duran Duran?" he informs me from his table. "Really I did. It was after a gig in Switzerland."

Now T. Rex comes on the playlist. "*Get it on, bang a gong ...*" Simon's little girls get up and start to dance. Both of them with their overalls still on, braids dangling. "What's that?" a look of joy in his eyes. "My girls like the song? You like this song, don't you?" Simon rises and starts to dance along with his little girls. It's a true sight to behold, the great Englishman with his long-flowing black hair and scarf, with the little girls in winter pants. Together they dance to T. Rex in the middle of the cafe. Razumova the real estate agent admires them, and so does Karolina, one of the owners, even as she works from her table. When the song finishes, Simon falls back into his seat with a laugh and seems more optimistic. Then he curses the weather.

"It's April now, do you realize?"

"It will get better."

"No, it won't. It snowed last year on St. John's Day. It never gets better. Only less worse."

I can't help but feel bad for him. There is no Duran Duran in Viljandi, Simon. There is no Simon Le Bon or Sting. Here one only finds bagpipes and accordions.

I don't have the heart to tell this to Simon though. One step at a time.

That night, the strangest dream about Simon ensues. In the dream, he loses his cool and goes down to the lake and starts cursing again. ("Goddamn bloody Estonians! Goddamn folk music! Goddamn weather! I used to party with Duran Duran! I used to party with Duran bloody Duran!") He's got a wall of speakers set up and he starts to blast *"Hungry Like the Wolf"* across the lake while he curses with such fury, and at such a volume that all the windows of Viljandi Town are opening and people are staring down at the troubled Englishman from the villas up on the hill. Another foreigner has gone berserk! Something must be done!

Mayor Timpson is up in the Old Water Tower with a set of binoculars. He is being given updates every minute on the minute. Soon they decide to dispatch Simon's Estonian lady down Trepimägi to stop the commotion, but Simon will not stop. The nervous breakdown continues. Suddenly, a large killer whale appears from Lake Viljandi, and Simon begins to dance because he is overjoyed by the whale. He dives in and I go running to the lake's shore. "Wait, Simon, come back! Don't do it!"

"Relax, mate," Simon says, now standing atop the killer whale as if surfing on its back. "He is my friend!" He smiles triumphantly and gives the whale a kiss.

Simon isn't the only one I dream about in Viljandi. Sometimes the Designer returns and stays at my place while she teaches at the Academy. As if things could get any worse, to have the most beautiful woman in the world as the best friend in the world, but to love her somewhere still.

She arrives on the train and I am there waiting. She disembarks with other Academy types and they talk of wool. Strange things they say. ("The love she feels, the love she feels for textiles," I once overheard one of these Academy people say.) The love I feel, the love I feel for her textiles. But that's all she thinks about. She irons her clothes again, then inspects her profile in the mirror. ("Is my hair better like this? Or up like this?") Then she takes everything off and starts over again.

At night we watch *Peaky Blinders* together and make dinner. It feels a little like home. My heart yearns for her, but at 11 PM, it's lights out, and she closes the curtain to the bedroom. Then one night, while I am sleeping on the couch, and she dozes behind the curtain in the big bed, I swear she comes to visit me in the wee hours, totally nude. It is something like a visit from a water spirit out of Arthurian Legend. The Lady in the Lake. In the legend, the water maiden waited for a wounded Arthur with two other ladies in black. The three maidens took him aboard their boat and sailed away to Avalon, comforting Arthur and pledging to heal his wounds.

The next morning at breakfast, I am moody indeed. Who the hell was this ghost woman to come back into my life again and again, and then leave, and then come back and even live with me. At night to crawl into bed with me and watch TV, and then just disappear again?

"What's your problem? Don't tell me you're going to start crying over me again."

"No."

"*Kas sa nutad või?*"

When I drop her off at the bus station, I confess the dream, but she just smiles at me. A pitying, but mischievous smile. The Designer has strange, foxlike eyes sometimes. She's like a character from *The Wind and the Willows*. Those eyes, those forest-like, foxlike eyes.

"So," she squints at me from beneath her cap. "You saw me naked then. *Sa nägid mind alasti.*"

"Yes," I say. There is a long, pregnant pause. "I'm sorry. I know we are just friends."

The Designer just shrugs. "*Normaalne,*" she says. "*Täiega.* Totally."

Such dreams I have here in Viljandi. Such wonderful dreams.

THE SOOTHSAYER

"Liberty stirs once more in the womb of time."
(Aleister Crowley (1875–1947), The Book of the Law,
1904)

The Soothsayer's apartment backs up to the old German Cemetery. To get there, I walk down Lossi Street, then past the St. John's Church and the Song Festival Grounds. Even on a weekend night all of it is bleak and vacant. On one side of the path, a series of steps leads up to an old graveyard where the von Ungern-Sternbergs, the wealthy owners of Viljandi Manor, are buried. I'm told that beneath the ancient manor house, there are secret haunted tunnels.

On the other side, steps lead down to the Ugala Theatre, and beyond are some newer houses, and then the cemetery. Never do I look at the German Cemetery, though. I know it's there, but I try to avoid it. There are about 700 Germans buried there. There are no grave markers, because the Soviets destroyed the graves. Only in the 1990s, did they restore the cemetery. To mark the tombs, a number of crosses were erected on the hill. Tonight, the crosses are in plain sight beyond the soothsayer's house and the orchards around it. A man has lashed his dog to one of the trees and it's howling. The soothsayer is at the door. She smiles a welcome.

The soothsayer. To start, there is something indeterminate about her. Vague. Obscure. I cannot describe her hair, which is both perfect and a mess, or even its color, or even what she looks like. I can't even remember how we first met, or how I found out about her. Usually in Viljandi, people suggest these kinds of miracle workers to you. "You should go and see Keiti in Peetrimõisa," or, "You should go and see Ülle Puu, the Tarot card reader. She'll set you straight. She knows it all."

She is a good-humored, jolly woman, with a delicate tickle of a voice, and I am warmly welcomed on her couch, into a room that's full of incense. Soon she is shuffling the cards. Shuffling, shuffling. She wears so many rings. Each finger is covered with pieces of metal and stone. "What do you want to know? What is it that you so badly want to know tonight?"

I glance down at my notebook. I don't know where to start.

"Don't you already know everything?"

She grins and pulls five cards from the pile and sets them down. She turns them over.

"Will you stay in Viljandi?" She closes her eyes and asks. Then she opens them.

"Well?"

"Yes, you will stay here. I don't see a ship. When people leave, I see a ship."

I shift in my seat. Somehow, I am fine with this fate.

"You don't have to do everything I advise, by the way. You should follow your heart."

"It's okay if I stay here."

"Oh."

"What?"

"You are in love with a woman too."

"Is that what the cards say?"

"But this woman, she is a Taurus."

"I thought she was a Gemini. The one I wrote to you about who went to Iceland."

"Not her. That's just some nonsense. This one here," she taps at the cards. "The Taurus."

"The Designer is a Taurus."

"The Designer?"

"Yes."

We both stare at the cards.

"I know you love her, honey, but she is not your woman. You think she is, but she's not."

"How do you know?"

"I just do."

"Then why is she always at my house? Why does she come naked to me in my dreams?"

"The cards say your future woman will not be this Taurus."

"Are you sure?"

The soothsayer laughs a very big laugh. "See, I told you that you were in love with the Taurus! But she is not your woman. Trust me, I used to date a Taurus. They are so stubborn."

I shake my head.

"I'm just saying you're lucky it's not her," says the soothsayer. "Unless you want to lock horns your whole life." She presses a finger down on another card. "I see an air sign, actually."

"An air sign? What are those?"

"Gemini, Libra, or Aquarius. Take your pick. But not this Gemini girl who ran away."

"Miss Cloud."

"She sounds a bit restless if you ask me."

It's not untrue.

"You don't believe me, do you? You are still stuck on the Taurus."

The soothsayer arranges the cards into a family constellation. My mother, father, children. Then she instructs me to draw a card for the Taurus. I pull the card and lay it by my side, but on the left. I stare at all the cards on the table, candle lights flickering. Outside the dog is still howling in the apple orchard. Those 700 German soldiers are still sleeping on the hill.

"You see," she says. "You put her on your left side. But the left side is where you might put a friend or a sister. Your partner should go on the right side. So put her on the right side."

I move the card to the right. As I stare at the cards though, something feels unstable and wrong. As if the card doesn't want to stay on the right. The card wants to be back on the left. The card is pulling itself back to the left, the way the sea current pulls you when the tide goes out.

"See. She is not your woman. Something doesn't feel right. Put the card back on the left."

We put it back on the left, and there it stays.

"You know, for a long time, I just didn't think I would make it," I say. "I really just didn't know what would happen. But I think my crisis is almost over and she has something to do with it. It's not just her. It's the energy that came with her. She opened the door to the new energy. I am writing better all the time now. I have new friends. Each day could be just perfect here. Yet I still don't feel healed inside myself. I still feel restless. I keep searching for something, for someone."

"All true," says the soothsayer, reshuffling her deck. "You won't be alone. An air sign will come and breathe new love into your heart. Still, you should follow your heart, as I said. Maybe it will be a water sign instead."

"What?"

"Kidding!" She covers her mouth like a guilty child. "What, you don't believe me? Are you going to start looking for a Pisces now, or a Cancer?"

"I believe you."

"Good."

"Why is she in my life then? Why does she keep coming back?"

"Do you really want to know?"

"Yes."

The soothsayer leans forward and whispers the answer in my ear. Then she laughs at my awed facial expression. "Oh my, honey, the look on your face."

"You really think so?" I ask. "Are you sure that's why she came?"

"Yes," she says. "I am quite sure of it."

JUST GET IT DONE!

"Viljandi right now is the best it's ever been. This place is like Estonia's San Francisco, there's a lot of new music coming out, weirdos walking around in red pants, that sort of thing."
(Paavo, a writer who moved to Viljandi.)

When May sets in, it's sunny and warm, and Viljandi becomes lush with flowers and foliage at last. Everything is as green as paradise, and I start to feel that I have woken from a long gray dream and found myself in heaven, or California maybe.

If you walk down Mäe Street, then up toward Liiva Street, there is a path you can take to cut through the terraces and gardens to get over to Roosi Street, and there is a magnificent villa overlooking the lake. In the bright evenings, I walk this path to savor all the nature.

One night I walk into the villa yard at 10 PM and a workman is still out putting the finishing touches on his labors. *"Jõudu tööle,"* I say to him. "Strength to work." He doesn't respond. "Oh, don't mind me," I say, walking closer, "I want to check out the house. Looks great." Still no response. The workman keeps carrying planks of siding to the scaffolding.

It's as if I'm invisible. As if I'm not even here.

In the yard at the cafe on another day, Enn puts up a structure to protect clients from the sun. There's a transparent roof, with dozens of tables beneath, each with a glass cistern of water flavored with slices of orange or floating cranberries. Sometimes, they have events back in the yard and violinists serenade clients from a raised platform. Once, the famous violinist Baltasar Montanaro came up from Marseille to play and all the girls cried. In the corner today, Vapp, the black cat, sits and licks his balls.

When you approach the cafe from the street, you just have to look over the fence to see who is at the cafe and decide if you want to join them or if you should keep going on your way, to another cafe perhaps. Maybe Simon is in there, depressed again.

On most days, though, I go in.

On this day, I am with Maaker the guitar player, who has long since shaved off his mustache. Between him and Enn sits Karoliina, that wonderful violinist from the band Tintura. She always seems to be seated at least two people away from me. Enn sits at the head of the table, his sleeves rolled up, his downy gray hair spotted with flecks of sawdust and a pink handkerchief dangling around his neck. Maaker is digging at a pile of potatoes and Karoliina has sunglasses on, but she cannot hide from Enn who is reminiscing about the first time he saw her lovely flaxen-head resting on the lip of a violin. "And she was so cute back then, you were what, 19?" he says.

Enn wants to think about the good old days because he has to get an Estonian driver's license now. There are several printed pages and a pen in front of him.

"I have to go and do it," he says in a somber tone, as if he has to go to prison for a while. "My old New Jersey license has expired."

"Here, let me see that," I take the papers. It's the usual run down. *Are you suffering from schizophrenia? Have you ever been depressed?* None of the boxes are checked. Sooner or later, we all have to go through this process. I learned the hard way, yet Enn has stubbornly avoided it.

Our Enn is going to be seventy-something in a few months. And he has to fill out paperwork for this? And he has to take a driving exam? With some *kid* observing him? As if he didn't know how to drive? Oh hell no. They even let Englishmen drive on the Estonian roads with their UK licenses, but Americans need to take a test? We're from the other side of the ocean, *terra incognita*. Enn looks at the document as if it was written in Japanese. He picks up the pen and drops it. He knows he must do it, but his will power hasn't manifested itself yet. The idea that he will soon sit in a car with a man a third his age who will assess his skills is a joke.

"How could they even fail me?" Enn despairs and chugs a throat-full of Colombian roast.

In the corner, Vapp the cat is still licking his balls clean. Deep in the yard, a pair of rickety steps leads up to a small terrace on the roof, surrounded by a railing and adorned with many flowering plants, a round table and chairs. A wiry man whom I have never seen before, is up on the terrace, watering the flowers. He looks down at me, and I look up at him, yet there is no exchange of friendly gestures. Instead, he squints at me as if he has never seen a man before and cannot believe his own eyes.

"Enn, who is that strange man?" I ask.

"What?" he looks up from his coffee.

"That strange man on the roof. Who is he?"

"Oh him?" he shrugs. "He's from Germany."

Somewhere out of sight, Enn's older sister Hela is muttering to herself in Estonian. Muttering loudly. She spent most of her life in Germany and so speaks her mother language with a German accent. The man, I take it, must be a German friend. The cat is still licking away in the sun. The strange man waters. Enn despairs. The cat licks. Then Paavo arrives to save us all.

Paavo is the author of *The Gogol Disco*. He is a real writer, one whom all others know to be this special thing called a writer. His novel, about a dystopian Viljandi under Imperial Russian rule, was made into a production at Ugala, and there have been four "Gogol Disco" parties in Viljandi since, the first one I attended in the fall of '16, where I got drunk and ended up wriggling on my back in a parking lot. That night a Finnish fellow named Pentti mistakenly tried to score some drugs off of me. I tried reading the book, but it's full of Russian slang words spelled with the Estonian alphabet. One character is named "Adolf Israilovitš Gukš." Was that some kind of in-the-know joke?

"It's being translated into Finnish, Latvian, Slovenian, Bulgarian, Czech," says Paavo, taking a seat at a table. "I am looking for an English translator, do you think you could do it?"

"I only translate children's books," I say. "I couldn't read it anyway. Too much Russian."

"You should learn Russian."

"I'm still learning Estonian."

"Well, my new novel *Black Sun* has Jamaican slang. Is that better?"

"You have a new novel out already?"

"Oh yes."

Suddenly the sun feels hotter. I think of all my half-started manuscripts. Were there five? Or seven? I think of my aching heart. I think of how I have so much inside me, so much material. So many thoughts, yet they never come out. I came to Viljandi to be just that, a writer. Instead, I'm hanging out with soothsayers by the German Cemetery. I'm crying about designers.

Paavo is slurping on a coffee, at ease in his skin. His force is so strong, he seems to emit his own gravitational pull. He's tugging me into his orbit. Paavo's a thick character, his spirit animal is no doubt a bulldog. His head is shaved, and he has tattoos of classic Estonian cartoons from the 1980s on his arms with funny little quips that look like the illustrations from *The Good Soldier Svejk*. He has a bunch of books in a little satchel he's keen to show me, as if he just harvested them from a shipwreck, one of which is Madonna's infamous *Sex* book from 1992, which shows the voluptuous pop star

Material Girl simulating fellatio on the rapper Vanilla Ice in a toilet, for instance. "Good pictures," says Paavo approvingly. I realize I have at last met someone in Viljandi I can talk to.

"So, what are you writing?" he asks over his shoulder as he flips through *Sex*.

"I am always writing something, mostly shorter pieces," I say. It's not a lie. The new *Postimees* column. The new *Hingele Pai* column. The new *Lõunakeskus* magazine column.

"Oh, no, no, no!" cries Paavo. "You mustn't waste your talent. You have to write a novel!"

"I did have an idea for a novel," I say, taking a seat opposite him. "It's about an Eskimo who moves to Estonia and becomes an ice cream delivery man. Then he falls in love with an Estonian woman, but she doesn't reciprocate or know how. He writes her love poetry but she doesn't react. He buys her flowers, but she complains, because she only likes flowers in the pot."

"That sounds like a children's book."

"But he's not only delivering ice cream. There's something else in the truck."

"This already sounds like a book for adults. You should write it. Submit it for *Kulka*. Cultural Capital. They fund writers."

"I did and they rejected it."

"What? *You* got rejected by Kulka? Then write something else, my friend! I write four hours every day. No plan. I just see where it goes. Slowly the book emerges. This goes over here, that goes there. So, I get my daily output, 7,000 or 8,000 characters. That's all. I can't do more."

I know he's right. I should write a novel like all of the Estonian writers around me. This is probably what I have been put in Viljandi to do. If there was ever a place to write a novel, this is it. Not Tallinn or Tartu. Here, in Viljandi. This is the place for gangster writers like Paavo. This is what the wiry men are really thinking as they water their flowers on the rooftops. Write something, write anything. Just a few hours! 8,000 characters. That's all. Then they will stage productions in your name, consecrate your work with the highest decorations, translate it into Bulgarian, Swedish, and Greek. You will no longer be an author, but an *auteur*.

Then you will come to the cafe and swap notes with Paavo about your grand work at little round tables under a hot May sun. Together you will roam the Viljandi lanes arm in arm, talking about what you're writing, but not disclosing too much. Just a taste. Just a taste. Literature will drip from you like sweet springtime birch juice. From this will come your own *Gogol Disco*, your own *Black Sun*. From this heart-broken wretch shall yet emerge a Man of Letters, a Viljandi god who cannot die.

"Remember," Paavo adds before he leaves. "Kerouac wrote *On the Road* in two weeks."

"Kerouac? How funny. I have his book *Big Sur* in my bag." I pull it out to show him.

"What's this?" he inspects the paperback. "You had Jack here with you, all along?"

"Jack was here with us all along."

"It's a sign! Two weeks is all you need. Two weeks and Enn's coffee. Just get it done!"

JAAK INSTRUCTS

"Freedom is what you do with what's been done to you."
(Jean-Paul Sartre (1905–1980), Situations IX, 1972)

At the back of the cafe the next day, there is Jaak the diplomat and the writer, sipping his latte. He sips it, savoring every taste, and then he sips again. No drop is wasted. Jaak wants to imbibe his drink, to become one with it. He has time to enjoy it, to let it sit in his mouth where he gargles it a bit. He's wearing sunglasses, and his fuzzy white pussycat face has its usual eternally bemused look to it. He is often bemused and indulges in the wonders of existence, every aspect. Then he takes another sip.

So goes the diplomat's morning coffee ritual.

"Where are you living these days, Jaak?" I say, taking a seat at his table. I was supposed to be writing my great novel, but Jaak always comes first. It's a small table, closer to the patch of rhubarb next to the fence. Jaak stares into the distance, pondering something, maybe something really big. He tilts his head, as a blind man might when encountering a strange sound.

Yet no answer comes.

"Has the foreign ministry dispatched you to Madrid?"

He bats the question away with a paw and grins.

"Lisbon?"

He does the same.

"Rome?"

"I am actually living in Uueveski," he purrs and leans in. The yard cat lies beside our table, sprawled out in the sun. It's a bold black cat – the one I call Vapp or "Crest" on account of the triangular patch of white on its chest. Jaak observes me watching this feline emperor.

"This one here was fighting before," Jaak whispers, "with that one, over there."

Jaak gestures at a brownish tabby patrolling the entrance to the cafe's back terrace. The black cat looks up and cries to the brown tabby – meow, meow, meow –- and Jaak under his breath mimics the desperate love cry – meow, meow, meow. A gentle chuckle. Jaak leans back and puts his hands behind his head, but not before taking another sip of coffee. "Ah," he says. "Spring!"

Time seems to stand still when Jaak sips his latte. Yet cats and coffee are not his only vices. He loves to talk of Italy, for instance, of the houses of Alberobello, or the dialect of the Genoese – "I was surprised by how different it is from Italian." One of his favorite honorary consuls is a Tuscan chianti magnate.

His iPad sits before him in a leather-bound case, his phone on top of that. Yet Jaak is never seen using either of these. They just accompany their larger master, mere trinkets or accessories of the diplomatic trade. This man before me is actually a former defense minister, a former UN ambassador, and his name has been passed around each time a president is selected. I'm actually rather grateful that they never chose Jaak to be president though, because I am not sure how American journalists would pronounce his last name, Jõerüüt. "*Joe – root?*" Just the thought of Wolf Blitzer calling him that on TV troubles me. No, let him remain Estonia's best kept secret, sipping his lattes, dreaming away in his Viljandi garden cafes about cats and chianti.

"Do you write?" I ask as he takes another sip. "I'm supposed to be writing."

"Oh, I am constantly writing. Constantly writing! Writing all the time, in fact."

Jaak stretches out his arms which find a natural place supporting the weight of his head. He yawns a bit and licks his lips, drifting off into another reverie. A springtime butterfly flutters by and lands for a moment on one of his arms and then it flutters off. Once in a while he will let you into his world of international affairs. These are governed by the genetic peculiarities of various neighboring peoples. The Swedes you very well know, are the Swedes. The Russians? Well ... "It's just in their DNA. It's just who they are."

He dreams on in quiet until another thought forms itself like a cloud.

"Venice!" he announces suddenly, dropping both hands to the table and grasping his coffee mug. "*Venezia!* Now there is a place I admire. It has everything. Its own language and culture. History. Why? It's like its own country!"

"It was once. The Venetian Republic. They ruled the Adriatic. Albania, Greece."

"Of course, of course," he purrs. Actually, Jaak doesn't say "of course." He says, *"Just."* This is his principal affirmation. "I just love Venice! God, I wish I was in Venice. *Just, just.*"

Jaak actually isn't from Viljandi, but his wife, the poet Viivi, grew up here and her mother still lives here in Uueveski. So Jaak comes and stays with his mother-in-law, just like he did some 40 years ago when she moved to town from Õiu, a little harbor village nearby on the shores of Lake Võrtsjärv. "That was in 1978 or 1979, I think," says Jaak as if it happened a few months ago. I like to hear his old stories, especially from the 1960s. His memoir, *On Nagu On* ("It is as it is") is full of anecdotes about this "hippie era," and has black-and-white photos of a bearded, Christ-like Jaak puffing away at cigarettes, pondering various existential questions.

My favorite Jaak story involves the visit of the French philosopher Jean-Paul Sartre and his companion Simone de Beauvoir to Estonia in the mid-1960s. According to Jaak, the Soviet secret services made sure that there was a French-speaking translator posted at every stop on Sartre and de Beauvoir's highly choreographed route. "These were actually well-known translators of French, like Ain Kaalep and Ott Ojamaa, but it was set up as if they just happened to be there, so that it would appear that the Estonian people happened to have a good command of French," chuckles Jaak. "They would just ask the crowd if anyone happened to speak French, and Ain, Ott, or someone would volunteer again. As if it all happened that way. *Juhuslikult.*"

On occasion when listening to these stories, I forget just how much history Jaak, or his wife Viivi, who sometimes joins him at the cafe, has seen. Jaak grew up on the outskirts of Tallinn, but Viivi is a local. She knows the Viljandi I have seen in those old photos snapped in the 1950s and 1960s that show a dusty remote farm town, where country ladies wearing handkerchiefs on their heads line up for bottles of milk, and even the posters of Comrade Stalin are foreign and unbelievable, as if they were all just part of an Ugala Theatre set design.

Back then there were other cafes for writers like us. Viljandi Cafe on Lossi Street was open, as it had been continuously since 1936. At Kirsimäe Maja, further down Lossi Street, there was Cafe Metropol, later renamed Cafe Oktoober. Viljandi's cafe culture was always here, it was just in different places. Long ago, before the advent of cafes, back in the 18th century, Viljandi had "friend's rooms," or *sõbratoad*. Viljandi people were always gathering like this, no matter the regime in power. But there was no Green House Cafe in Jaak's youth. There was no Layk. And there was definitely no Uku Keskus, the large shopping center that at one time in the distant past served as a grim prison. It is here, on the terrace of Uku, where Jaak and Viivi can be spotted sipping coffees procured in the early hours from Hesburger, the Finnish fast-food chain. Jaak the diplomat, man of letters, chum of Italian chianti barons, is not ashamed of this at all.

"Good coffee is just good coffee," he says.

Back at the Green House Cafe, where his latte is still half full, I broach other topics to get a rise out of Jaak. Russia. NATO. EKRE. These topics bore Jaak until I mention writing.

"I read somewhere that you were writing miniatures. But what is a miniature? Is it a tiny book? And do you have to use a small pen to write one?"

"No, no, no, no, no, no," he says. "It's nothing like that."

"What is it like?"

"These are small, compact pieces. It's quite funny you know, in English you have the novel, but in Estonian we have a *romaan*, which is a longer book. But *novellid* are more like novellas, shorter pieces. And then there are anecdotes, which in English are just interesting stories, but in Estonian, they are meant to be funny. Anecdotes versus *anekdootid*, novels versus *novellid*. It's as if everything is a bit skewed, or upside down or backward in the translations."

"I still would like to write miniature books with a small pen," I say.

"But then write away, Petrone! Write some fascinating tiny books! Just pretend that the Green House is Cafe Greco in Rome and away you go." He stalls for a bit to savor this idea in the sun, quite satisfied with his impromptu writing lecture. Then his eyes wander ever so slowly to his phone, which still sits idly soaking up the sun. In the corner, Vapp yawns and scratches himself.

"Oh my God! Just look at the time!" Jaak exclaims and sits up.

"What's wrong?"

"I have to catch a train!"

"To where?"

"To Tallinn, of course. I must go now."

"What are you doing in Tallinn?"

He puts on his shades again. "I have a very important meeting," he says.

"An important meeting? With whom?"

No further details. Jaak wishes me *adieu* – he uses this word, and then *arrivaderci* – he uses this word too. He shakes my hand. Then he mounts his bike – the gray hair, the beard, the sandals – and with a wave our Jaak is gone, the last dregs of his latte left evaporating in the sun.

LUNCH WITH KANGILASKI

"I feel Viljandi is a special bubble, where being different is allowed. One can float through the town easily, with some little, easily solvable obstacles, sometimes slowing down, sometimes going down the hill a bit faster, and finally ending at the delta of the lake, where some brave people meet up to refresh their souls in winter, and socialize in spring, summer, and autumn."
(Daniel Hozjan, a teacher who moved to Viljandi from Switzerland.)

There's a kind of drift that comes over you when you've been in Viljandi for a long time. People flow into and out of your life. One day it's Paavo, the next day it's Jaak, and the third day, it's Pepi the Argentinian. The Designer comes and goes. Sometimes she makes little helpful suggestions to me. What foods I should eat, what teas I should drink. Buy this couch, not that couch. Then she gets mad at me when I rearrange my furniture the wrong way, and then I have to put my couch back to where it used to be. The Designer implores me to invest in a dishwasher. She's trying to take care of me, as I understand. She actually does care about me.

But then she leaves and life here is all drift. Every day is the same sort of day, maybe just a little different. But I suspect, more than ever, that Viljandi is a kind of dreamy place, a limbo for lost souls, where you can come to work through problems, as she once told me, so long ago.

The drift brings me back to the cafe on a sunny summer day where I see the illustrator Kangilaski is having lunch with her son. Our Kangilaski, the truest *artiste*. At some point, to remind herself, she had the Estonian words for left and right tattooed on her forearms.

The special of the day is beef and beet cutlets, in the style of the Swedish dish Biff à la Lindström, with boiled potatoes and a white sauce with a hint of horseradish. Kangilaski forks one of the smaller potatoes into the boy's mouth. In the corner, a blonde dressed all in white is reading a magazine. She has a gold bracelet around her wrist, and rings on most of her fingers. She wears sunglasses too, but what catches my eye most are her legs, which are supple and long and tanned. I know she must be from Tallinn because only women from Tallinn dress that way.

I sigh.

"What is it?" asks Kangilaski. She is one of the best illustrators in the country, in my opinion. And like Maaker and all of the other Viljandi artists, she is always pushing herself to be better. Kangilaski has two books to finish at the moment, yet shows no apparent signs of stress. She wears sunglasses and munches on. Kangilaski has a lanky frame, dark hair, a dry sense of humor. She can also be quite sarcastic. Yet she shows kindness toward me now and then too. I am always happy to have lunch with Kangilaski. Her first name is Kristi, but there are just so many Kristis in Viljandi, not to mention Kerstis. This is why I call them all by their last names.

"I'm just a bohemian," I say. "Look at me," I tug at my Nepali shirt. "I wear this shirt. I hang around cafes. I am supposed to be writing, but I just talk. *Ühesõnaga*, I'm a loser."

"Where do you think you should be then?"

"In Tallinn, of course! I should wear a jacket and tie. Have an office job, a nice car. Maybe have a gig at one of those start-ups. Stop hanging out with all of these lunatic bohemians! I should have a house in Kakumäe. Go to all those concerts and restaurants. Like a real person. Then I should take vacations to cool places and take pictures of myself enjoying the vacation. Post it all on Instagram. See how many likes I get. That's what real life is actually about."

"Don't you worry," says Kangilaski. "You just sit here and keep writing like you do. One day, some girl with a Nepali shirt will show up. That's all you have to do. Just keep writing."

"Funny you mentioned that. Once, years ago, I did see a girl with a Nepali shirt in Viljandi. She had blond hair and wore a red Nepali shirt. She was reading a book in Fellin."

"Did you talk to her?"

"No. I was married then."

Kangilaski gives me a strange look as if she cannot connect these two pieces of information.

"And you were afraid to talk to her because ..."

"I just didn't feel like talking to her. She was very beautiful though."

I look around the yard for a moment and then remember that spring, when the street's cobblestones glistened after the rain. I remember hearing some sad pop song on the radio, and that feeling that sooner or later the wave of my life was going to crash down. I knew it then and it was a terrifying feeling. Because, like it or not, we are all victims of nature.

"I think I remember seeing this girl. The one with the Nepali shirt that you saw. I used to see her around. I haven't seen her recently though."

We both look around as if she might appear. Kangilaski feeds her son more potatoes.

"I have no idea what happened to her," I say and then I look away again. The truth is, I can't remember if I had actually seen the girl anymore. My memories and dreams are blurring and fusing together in Viljandi. In the corner, the lady in white with the tanned legs is now tinkering with her phone, sipping coffee. "Who knows where she went," I say.

Kangilaski is a hub of information in Viljandi. Between Kangilaski, Laineli, and Heldi, I think most things are known. Once I went for a walk alone and Heldi told me later she had heard I went for a walk, because I had walked by Laineli's window. They know everything about me. Though Kangilaski senses my attachment to the Designer, she has warned me to not fall in love.

"Forgive me for saying this," she tells me, "but the Designer is a bit too *karm* for you."

"*Karm*?"

"Harsh, austere, strong willed."

I'm too soft and fluffy for such a person. Such a person needs a man who can match her strength. Someone who can "put her in the frying pan," to use one of Kangilaski's pithy country girl idioms. It's true, but I feel inadequate.

My mother wanted me to be someone else, a politician perhaps, someone with status and power. My ex-wife was disappointed with me because all I want to do is hang out in cafes. I'm just not strong enough to be attractive to the Designer. And the only romantic gesture I made after the end of my marriage resulted in a girl fleeing to a desolate island in the middle of the North Atlantic.

And yet I cannot give up! I have to move forward! I must take Kangilaski's advice: "Wait for the girl in the Nepali shirt," and "just keep writing."

THE SIRENS

"A group of friends' tragic weekend. Viljandi youth remember three friends, of whom one died in an accident while leaping from the diving tower at Lake Viljandi, and the others were found dead in a hotel in a Ukrainian summer resort. The Estonians thought they had bought cocaine from a local dealer, but it was amphetamine, sold under the moniker, 'salt.'"
("Sakala" newspaper, 2018)

That night we hear sirens, the awful wail of tragedy. This in a quiet town, where police are seldom seen and almost never heard. One after the other, they speed down to the lake. I'm in the room of the small apartment when it happens, the one that the Designer is renting with her younger sister, known to all as "Pets," a short form of Peeter, on account of her short-cropped blond hair and tomboy interests. "Pets" does not protest this. She's a bit of a rebel. The Designer is tired after work, stretched on the couch. Yet even she's surprised by the noise.

"What the hell is going on out there?"

The story around the lake incident is related the next morning in the woodshop of Vilma House by none other than DJ Jaanika as she works together with half a dozen young women to stitch together the stage decorations for the up-coming Viljandi Folk Music Festival. The ladies crouch over prints of 19th century Viljandi shepherds, or Seto ladies in regalia. In the late hours, patterns are being embroidered into sheets of plastic mole fencing with used CDs and cloth.

"There were two drunk guys on the diving platform, at the highest level," says Jaanika. "One was on the other's shoulders. When they dove together, the top one hit his head on the platform. He was dead before he hit the water. His pregnant wife was on the beach. She saw it all. My friend knows this girl. She says she's a cool chick, but yeah, those guys are real *ossid*."

"Were *ossid*," someone says.

"I know," says Jaanika. "It's really sad. *Kurb*!"

"What's an *oss*?" I ask.

"Petrone, how could you live in Estonia for 16 years and still not know what an *oss* is?"

This is what Pets asks me, rising up from her folk pattern work. Pets is part of the core team. At night, she sleeps beside the Designer in bed. They hold each other, like kittens or twins. The Designer keeps a black-and-white photo of them as children holding each other. She displays it every apartment she moves into. She has a notebook into which she has sketched the designs for the decorations with pencil outlines of shepherds and Seto women. The actual decorations take up most of the floor in the back of the woodshop. Three women might work on one banner at a time. This is all they do, all day long.

"Are *ossid* like *rullnokad*?" I ask. *Rullnokad* is another sub-culture of young men, known for the way they roll the beaks of their caps.

"More or less. You know. They have shaved heads and hang out in parking lots drinking. A lot. *Ossid* drink a lot."

One less *oss* in Estonia then, but at what cost? Every year many young men die senseless deaths that come from mixing drinks with sport. The population registry ticks down. I think of the conservative politicians who are so concerned about immigration. Yet the true enemies of the nation might not be Muslim refugees. They might be the Estonians themselves.

Pets is the anti-*oss*. She adheres to a very strict vegan diet. Much of Pets' food is sourced from supermarket dumpsters. At night, she and the Designer roll around town in a British-made Peugeot, rummaging through the garbage bins behind Maxima and Konsum, hoping to pluck up a bag of apples, pears, bananas, or turnips. On several nights I have joined them, poking through fermenting cakes to pull a few bananas or beets from the bottom. These are then blended into smoothies, or big pots of steaming soup – which I call "garbage soup" – which they flavor with spices. When I eat it, I let the soup settle into my mouth, savor every taste, trying to detect any traces of mold or rot, but I cannot. Then I swallow it all. Curried beets and potatoes. *Maitsev!*

One morning, this same Pets offers me a steaming cup of something called *chaga*, a tea made from a fungus that grows on birches and is alleged to have detoxifying properties.

"Long ago, the Estonians would drink this to cleanse themselves," Pets says.

I stared down into the dark tea.

"Does it have any psychedelic properties? Like maca?"

"Yes," Pets says. "But you would have to drink a lot of it to hallucinate."

"In that case, I'll drink the whole bottle."

"No, you won't," she says. "Because it's mine."

This is what people who aren't *ossid* in Viljandi drink. Black fungus tea. Sometimes coffee too. We have two moka espresso makers in the apartment, one large, one small. The big one is called "senior" the smaller one "junior." And so, the Designer will ask. "Petrone, will you make us more coffee?"

"Junior or senior?"

"Senior."

This is what we drink as the ambulances speed down the hill.

Back in the woodshop, Pets is working on a large black-and-white print of two shepherds taken at the Castle Ruins about a century ago. In an adjacent room, another young woman who works for the Designer sits at a sewing machine working with long runs of shiny reflecting silver material and listening to electronic music. This silvery stuff will eventually be suspended above people at the festival. The inspiration came from the Designer's recent trip to Mallorca. In the streets of Mallorca, they hang the same silvery material overhead and it jingles in the breeze.

The Designer is always at work designing, you see. Even while on vacation, she is designing. She's at the beach and her assistants are carrying out logistics. Bring that box here. Take that bag there. Acquire X amount of mole fencing. NB! Contact print shop.

During that same trip, which also took her to Barcelona, I also received a few messages to go to a shop down the street one day to pick up a few bags of scrap material, which I did, lugging the bags back to the apartment over my shoulder. I didn't bother to ask what was in the bags because I knew how the Designer would respond: *"Ma ei viitsi sellest rääkida."* "I just don't feel like talking about it." She doesn't waste words when logistics are involved, as she just needs to know if you will do it or not. If not, she will assign the task to somebody else. The point is to accomplish the task. Time is of the essence! She is not actually rude, although some might think so. She is not actually inconsiderate, although some might whisper that she is egocentric. She just is an organizer who wants to get things done. Not that she is always so precise.

In the morning, with her hair in her face, she yawns and drifts over to the small moka coffee maker and waits for it to boil while her cat looks up longingly at his mother, needy for her affection. Somehow, it's reassured that once again the lady who loves him can meet his needs.

She cleans herself up, pulling her golden locks up into a bun, donning a white blouse that breathes and moves with her shape, a black skirt that somehow brings to mind Italy of the 1950s. I feel somehow captivated by this person's presence and even a pinch jealous: how can she organize so well? How can she keep herself so together? I'm a flakey, pulsating, disorganized mess. She's running a team of mini-designers who live to do her bidding. They ask, she instructs.

"You shouldn't compare yourself to other people," she says when I express these feelings.

That night, I head out for my regular evening walk. I like to amble down Õuna Street, look up at the houses, their gardens and terraces. You can pick raspberries along the way and there is a good view of the lake. Leo Normet, the composer of the popular postwar song, "*Puhkuse veedame kõik Viljandis* (We all spend our vacation in Viljandi)" used to live in one of these houses.

I pause to admire the lake and walk toward the center of town. I have a book in my knapsack. I sit down at one of the vacant tables outside the Grand Hotel Viljandi. There I begin to read a few pages of "Grace" by James Joyce, about a man who passed out in a Dublin urinal whose name no one could recall. Something feels off, and I can't put my finger on it. An eerie fog settles in around midnight. I'm feeling unsettled now, so of course, the man they call Köler has to join me. He's still got on his old-fashioned hat. His hair is long, graying, and greasy.

"Greetings to our national writer," he announces. "*Tere, rahvakirjanik!*"

He takes a seat opposite me at the table, holding a small white cup in his hand.

"You're drinking coffee at midnight?"

"Of course," he says. "The Grand Hotel is the only place in town where you can get a cup of coffee at midnight." He takes a sip from the cup, and I suddenly feel the urge to get one too.

"Tell me, Köler," I say to the old man. "What exactly is an *oss*?"

Köler lights a cigarette, holds the smoke in his lungs, and exhales.

"And how are *ossid* related to *rullnokad*?"

"This may be hard for you to understand, since you are one of the *Il Duce* people," Köler begins, "but decades ago the Soviets began to undertake a project to create a new kind of man. This man they called *Homo sovieticus*. You see, before there was *Homo sapiens*, but *Homo sovieticus* was the next step in evolution. *Homo sovieticus* doesn't care about anything. He is indifferent to all. Whatever he is told to do, he will do it. To relax, he drinks or takes drugs. He doesn't know what love is. He's unaware that he even has a heart. That is *Homo sovieticus*."

"But this process is over. There is no more Soviet Union. Lenin is dead."

Köler nearly keels over with laughter at this statement. "No, my boy, Lenin is not dead! Haven't you heard? Lenin is immortal!" More big laughs. "Just give me a few more moments. Oh! Lenin is dead! That's a good one. Look, this process is now beyond the control of those who devised it anyway. It is ongoing, my boy. It goes on! Because *rullnokad* are the sons of *Homo sovieticus*. And *ossid* are the sons of *rullnokad*. *Ossid* are therefore the grandsons of *Homo sovieticus*. Nothing can stop this process. So, it will go on and on, until the end of time."

It's a dire forecast, but it seems to fit with what will turn out to be a weird summer.

THE THING ABOUT FOLK ...

"The thing about Folk in Viljandi is that anything goes, all is allowed, permitted. Well, not everything but, well, yes, actually everything, everything is allowed during Folk."
(Romet Koser, an actor and a clown from Viljandi.)

It starts off innocently enough, with a musician in knickers playing folk songs on his accordion in the shade of the Old Fire Station on Väike-Kauba Street. The music sounds very innocent and free on Thursday. But by Sunday, I am convinced folk music is the devil's music.

The Designer and I are barely on speaking terms by Sunday. Her sister Pets, the rebel vegan, left early that morning. She has just packed her things into her Peugeot, and then leaves without saying goodbye. At dawn I watched her through the window as she hurried off, and I am completely perplexed by the turn of events.

During the festival the Designer spends most of the time in a wild feverish state. Most mornings she doesn't return until 5 AM. Then she's off somewhere with someone, at the lake swimming in the nude at twilight. "I've worked so hard this year," she says. "All I do is work, work, work! Can't I ever just enjoy myself?"

There are all kinds of characters in and out of the apartment. Kerttu the Photographer is sleeping there, and before her, someone who might have been the Designer's boyfriend was in there. People are in and out sitting around, drinking beer and playing harmonicas and it starts to irk me. There is nothing to be done though. If you live in Viljandi during the folk festival, your home is everybody's.

I know these are Estonians and in Estonia there is your thing (*"sinu asi"*) and my thing (*"minu asi"*) and my thing is not your thing (*"minu asi pole sinu asi"*). If you ask, then you have overstepped some line. *"Aga see pole tegelikult sinu asi."* "But that's not your thing, actually."

All of the people though, all of the energy, it starts to wear me down. My residual romantic feelings for this girl who disappears and comes crawling in at 5 AM. The characters who climb through the windows.

As soon as the festival is over, the Designer leaves too, without any notice. One day, she's just gone. The bicycle is there, the window is open, but she is nowhere to be seen or found. Before she left, she had taken every last item of mine from the small apartment, put it in a box, and left it on my kitchen table. It means something but whatever that is I cannot say.

By the third day, Saturday, my own life has descended into filthy squalor. Heldi, the event planner from Järvamaa, is sleeping on my couch because she has rented out her own place to some friends. At some point, she has a major fight with her boyfriend over the phone and I am forced to leave while they scream at each other. Something about Kilingi-Nõmme. I can hear them yelling through the windows. "Kilingi-Nõmme! Kilingi-Nõmme!" Later, they make up.

Meantime, a strange cat starts coming in the windows and sleeping beside us in the evenings. It's a gray cat, small and with a dopey, vulnerable look on its face. The cat is female and during most of the day, it sits staring down into one of the street's sewers. People have theories about why it spends so much time staring into it. Maybe one of its kittens fell in? You must also think of how interesting Viljandi is for cats too. All of these alleyways, and cellars, broken houses, and gardens, are loaded with other cats. And then consider the strangers' apartments, strangers like me, who somehow allow a cat called Sewer Cat to sleep beside them.

The scene around the Ait is anarchic. There are people everywhere. There is so much music, it sounds as if someone blew up a music store. At one point, I see my own daughter Anna walking through the crowds. This little 11-year-old strides forward through the masses with a sense of purpose on her way to buy some sea buckthorn juice. I call out to her but she doesn't respond. She is soon swept away by all the Tallinners who have come to see Curly Strings.

After a concert by a folk group from Italy, I stand in line behind local girls in white dresses who have come to have their breasts autographed by the swarthy musicians. Even the bashful and self-effacing singer, Riccardo, who couldn't thank the crowds enough for their love and support, cannot refuse their requests to have him write his name on their flesh. When I relate the scene to a small crowd of friends and acquaintances on Kirsimägi, I receive a lecture from Virgi, of all people, the legendary teacher from the Viljandi Free Waldorf School.

"Young man, these women have endured 50 years of Soviet occupation!" Virgi chides me. "They have earned the right to have their breasts autographed by some hot Italian guys."

The next morning, I awake fully clothed with a fly buzzing around my face. Sweat, sweat all over. To the cafe at once! It takes three coffees to get me fully on my feet.

I stare at the tablecloth wet with grease and coffee stains, empty water glasses, a sugar jar, and a vase of flowers, sweating, more moisture in the sun. Jõeste is here, reading the newspaper while eating an apple. I vaguely recall drinking *handsa* in a parking lot at 3 AM with the Designer who I am convinced is trying to kill me. "Just stay out more. Hang with us!" Every time I try to slip away, she's there. "Where do you think you're going? No, you are not going to sleep. You have to stay out longer!" And the soothsayer thinks that this is the person who is my guardian angel? My lady in the lake? Hmm.

When I burst into the room that morning in a particularly exuberant and festive mood, the overtired Designer scolds me for intruding on her and her many girlfriends' sacred privacy and all, and calls me an "asshole." This sets what's left of my self-worth into precipitous freefall.

Luckily, Merit finds me moping at the cafe, swoops in, and bails me out.

Merit and Aivar's estate is located on the margins of Viljandi overlooking beautiful Karula Lake. You can see it from the road when you drive by. The rows of trees on both sides of the road make me feel as if I am being whisked away to some French chateau in Merit's car. "There are always lows in life," Merit tells me. "The trick is to learn not to dwell on them. So that the lows are less low."

Heldi is with us. Together we are ensconced on the back terrace by the lake. Merit brings out a bottle of wine, which we drink up quickly, and then another. Soon after, Heldi tears off her clothes and jumps in the lake. Then she climbs onto a giant trampoline and begins to leap in the nude. There is a naked 41-year-old woman jumping on a trampoline. She stretches out her arms as she jumps. "Come on, Justin!" she cries. "Take your clothes off too! Come swimming!"

I walk down to the dock, look around, and quickly tug down my bathing suit. Then I dip into the lake. I swim around to another dock and a set of stairs, pull myself out, and rest a bit in the sun. I feel exposed by all the emotional tumult of Folk.

Why does everything with the Designer always have to get so out of hand? It was making me break inside. "You two just have some kind of connection," Merit informs me later, as we drink yet another bottle of cold white wine. "You are sensitive to each other and get under each other's skin. I do believe she cares about you. She's an artist, too. She might not show it, but she's just as sensitive as you are."

I sprawl on my belly on one of the long chairs by the lake. Merit comes and sits in a chair beside me. She still has her sunglasses and swimsuit on. She reclines and reaches to take my hand in hers. "Don't read too much into this, but I think you need this right now," she says. "You can hold my hand for as long as you need." I hold her hand until I am ready and let go.

Merit rises and walks majestically down to the lake. There is sun all over her and it reflects off of her and the water. Everything is wonderful, shimmering and warm here at Karula. With the water at her chest, she turns and waves. Then she dives into the lake and swims away.

A FIGHT IN THE STREETS

"We all spend our holidays in Viljandi, because that's where paradise is."
(Leo Normet (1922–1995), song "Holiday in Viljandi," 1959.)

On a cool September morning, outside Romaan, a group of thick youths in dark coats line the street, watching as two of them go at it like animals. I tell you, to see another man trying to hurt another man, it makes you sick, like you want to vomit all up and down Koidu Street.

Instead, I take refuge in the toilet in Romaan, staring at the portraits of politicians Indrek Saar and Jevgeni Ossinovski on the wall. Neither of these Social Democrats look particularly happy in their official Romaan toilet portraits, but at least they aren't killing each other like those idiots. I can hear them outside. I hear the thud of flesh on flesh. I have no stomach for violence.

The way the local boys do it is they line up for the big fight. It reminds me of those hunters you see out on the country roads in autumn, all lined up wearing their orange vests. The locals wear dark coats, hats. It's hard to tell any one of them apart from each other. They won't let anyone intervene though. The fight is on, and there is a fight. At least until the police show.

"They want to have their fight, let them have their fight," one of them told the Chef when he tried to stop them. His friend, another Swede named Erik with curly tufts of premature gray hair and a fisherman's beard, is put off by the whole spectacle. In Sweden, they just don't do things this way. In Sweden, they just ride their bikes around and wave to each other and smile.

"No, no, no," Erik says pacing back and forth. "This just isn't done. This just isn't done!" He says it as if someone has put too much sugar on some Swedish cinnamon buns.

I've got five tequilas in me but it's not of my making. The Designer is back and she's been urging me to drink all night. There's a certain terror that arises when I see her, as if she's come to collect my soul. I first saw her coming through the bushes dressed all in white like the angel of broken dreams. The hair. The eyes. She is striking, but something is burning her up inside and it's not just me. She'll never say what it is, or what happened, or if it's something else entirely. Whatever it is, it's big. "You just don't know! You have no idea what's actually going on!"

What is actually going on with her? I haven't got a clue.

At Romaan, they give you the shot on a wooden board with the lime and a pinch of salt. That's what you get. I was out in the street licking salt off a piece of oak when I first caught a whiff of the storm. A younger Estonian had come charging out of the gates of Romaan cursing.

"I hate this country!" he said to me. "I hate this country and all the people in it."

"But you are from this country," I said, licking the board. "You are one of these people."

"You don't know. You don't know Estonians. You don't know how evil they are!"

"But you are an Estonian. You are one of them too."

"Not in my heart, I'm not! Not in my heart!"

This poor kid, a youth of 30 at the most. He didn't look like a killer, more like a boy who had just had too much. Maybe he had just lost his job at the pillow factory, or his girlfriend had dumped him, or he had a fight with his stepfather. Some trivial inconvenience. He wasn't having any insults though. Whoever it was who had said the wrong thing to him was going to pay for it.

He wanted a fight and the local boys weren't going to stand in the way.

The police had indeed rolled through earlier in their blue-and-white cruiser. It was the usual late-night patrol. Romaan though is more often a subdued place. This is Pepi the Argentinian's turf. Pepi does not get in fights, as you very well know. He speaks of peace and love and jams on his guitar, and says only peaceful and lovely things. Half his head is shaved, and he has a nail in one of his ears and sports a bead necklace. He stands in the yard playing table tennis with the others, and on occasion some of the better known Ugala actors will show up and engage him in this riveting game. Sometimes, Bruno, the Austrian businessman, will have a turn.

Romaan is usually a peaceful place. It's over at Cheers on Lossi that you get the real action. One can be sure that there will be three or four locals engaged in either a shouting match or a brawl tonight. The police park across the street and wait for it, like patient ice fishermen. All they have to do is sit and wait.

At some ungodly hour later, I am at Vanalinna Burger. Platters of fries are consumed, and then the cheeseburgers come out. The Chef, the Designer, Erik, and the Designer's cousin, are all gathered around a table. A strange peace descends as the Designer engages in conversation with the Swede Erik. He compliments her hair and she compliments his beard. The Designer seems to have calmed down.

The Chef was there when the local boys moved in and broke it up. "They were just watching to make sure it didn't get out of hand. When it did, they pulled them apart. I did too. You should have felt how strong that kid was! It took four of us to get him off of the other one."

The Chef is in a rotten mood. He's in a rotten mood because he doesn't like the way his burger has been cooked. "To think that they call this a burger place," he grumbles and looks around. "They call this a burger place and they can't even make a decent burger!" He tosses his food into a heap of fries. "That's it. I'm going to do something about it." He stands up and goes in the back. There is a heated discussion with the fry cook, which I can only barely follow because of the noise from the kitchen. "Do you know," I hear him say, "do you know how much love goes into the creation of this beef?

The love, the love of the farmer who raises the cow? The love of the slaughterer, who with his hands must take life from this sweet animal so that we might eat ..."

Erik covers his eyes with one hand, only to peek out between his fingers.

"... The love," the Chef goes on, "the love of the butcher who cuts up the poor cow's body. The love of the machinist, who grinds the meat into burgers. But you ... you have no love! You have no respect for love! You have no respect for food! You just take this meat, this labor of love, and you put it on your grill. And then you fry it until it tastes like a damn hockey puck! Let me school you on the proper way to cook a burger. Let me teach you the meaning of respect!"

"I think he's going to get an Academy Award for Best Actor," I say.

"Indeed," Erik says.

The Chef strides at last back to the table, slides into his seat. He looks tired but at least satisfied. "We had a good talk," he says. "He promised he will never burn a burger ever again."

The next morning, we have coffee together in the cafe's courtyard. It's a brilliant autumn day, with good sun, and it seems all the turbulence has passed. Whatever it is between me and the Designer again has calmed. She tells us all that Erik is on his way. Looking at the Designer now, I feel that our story is at least for now resolved. It is just as the soothsayer had warned me months before. She is not my woman. Sometimes I think she is, but she is not. Her card belongs on the left. If I lift the card and try to place it on the right, there is a rupture in the space-time continuum. The tomb of the undead is opened, and all kinds of macabre creatures crawl out. Better to put the card back on the left where it belongs. Better to keep that crypt sealed off tight.

So, it goes with our peculiar kind of friendship.

Somewhere the two boys from the fight are sleeping off their war wounds. Maybe they can't even remember what happened, or why. And to think the evening had started off peacefully and quietly enough without any hint of trouble. There were two women in front singing *runo* songs when I arrived at Romaan. Those layers of choruses. Somehow, they knew all the words.

THE GOLDEN KRINGEL

"Three local drunks came down the street, one in a pair of yellow workman's overalls. They have occupied the tiny park bench beside Romaan, which serves as a gathering place for these lucky few. 'Hey mate, you got a light?' asks one. But the other – in the yellow overalls – stops him. 'Don't bother him,' he says. 'He's a writer."
(From my journal, 2018.)

One fall day, my daughter calls me up and tells me she needs to come home because she needs a pack of yarn for her handicrafts class, or *käsitöö* as it's called, which she hates. I agree to meet her at the Green House Cafe and then we will walk over. To see this child of mine coming up Tartu Street from the window of the cafe, face to the wind. Somedays she looks quite like her mother, other days she looks like someone from my family. Her whole body is *Pugliese* in origin. Many of her friends are pale, thin, and lean.

I sometimes come home and there are three or four Viljandi girls sitting on my couch and they all look the same. My child, our child, is ruddy and robust. There is a touch of the Greek in this girl of mine. This is neither here nor there. This lost little Greek girl needs more yarn and a needle, a *heegelnõel*. At the fabric store on Lossi Street, she digs through the piles of yarn or *lõng*. Then she decides on a big bunch of yellow and pink.

"I'm not sure why I need to learn this Waldorf stuff," she says. "I want to be a chemist."

"Well, what else are you learning in school?"

"Hindu Gods. Somebody named ... *Siddarth*? Or something like that."

"You're learning about Siddartha? That's fantastic. I wish I was."

"I just want to grow up and move to Stockholm and be a chemist."

"Don't you want to stay in Viljandi?"

"Are you kidding me? Viljandi sucks."

"Why Stockholm then?"

"Then I can go to *Gröna Lund*, the big amusement park, whenever I want."

I put an arm around her. "I promise I will do all I can to make your dreams come true."

I walk her back to the school. On the way back, I duck into Ormisson for a hot cup of green tea.

This building that houses the Park Hotell Viljandi and Restoran Ormisson has always caught my eye. Many years ago I would walk by the large ruined castle, along that little path that runs between it and the park, the one that they still call *Hiire tänav* – "Mouse Street" – and I feel it breathing down on me with those big windows. It's another of Viljandi's gorgeous mansions, I think. I was told that in 1910, the local Ormisson family built it. How did they make so much money to afford a four-story Bavarian-style villa in town? Agriculture, it was said. Around the time of the American Civil War, Viljandi County became one of the top exporters of flax in the world. This money made the locals fantastically wealthy. Thus, they became proper bourgeois Estonians.

So, it was for the Ormissons. At their new castle in the center of town, they needed servants, kitchens, and a master suite. They needed the luxuries befitting the men of great wealth. This was the purpose of this building. Villem Ormisson, scion of the family, became an important impressionist painter. It is for him that the restaurant is named.

Around the time of the First World War, the building was transitioned into a hotel. In fact, the Park Hotell Viljandi used to be called the Grand Hotel Viljandi. After the Soviets took over, it was repurposed as a school and the Grand Hotel moved to the corner of Lossi and Tartu Streets.

The school was abandoned and in recent years stood empty. Birch trees even sprouted in its atrium. Now the atrium is enclosed by a beautiful glass roof. There is an old-fashioned elevator, and of course the restaurant is run by our friend the Chef. He's back from his Oslo sojourn with coke-sniffing chefs and blow-up dolls. He's in charge now, a man who has great responsibilities. Not that he looks like it. He's grown his hair out even longer. He looks like he should be the leader of some outlaw Mexican motorcycle outfit. Those hired to work in the restaurant revere him though. The people here call him "boss".

A golden *kringel* pastry, the symbol of bakeries in Estonia, hangs above the restaurant's door. For this reason, I call this establishment the Golden Kringel. It's my new writing haunt.

In the kitchen below the restaurant, the cooks Miguel, who is Portuguese, and Ebo, who is from Ghana, are putting the finishing touches on the salads for some small-town bourgeois reception. Maybe the mayor will show this time. The orange-yellow tomatoes, the sprinkle of sprouts, the grind of the peppermill. There is an artistry in that, for we are all artists here in Viljandi.

In the mornings, I am joined by the Chef, Miguel, and Ebo for breakfast. They both shake my hand and hug me when they see me each day at Ormisson. We are brothers now, I think. Brothers of the Golden Kringel.

A cold snap brings out the red in the leaves and the morning is astonishing and pretty. At breakfast at Ormisson, the Chef, Miguel, and Ebo eat and make morning conversation. Ebo is a big man with a deep, husky voice. He wears a gold earring in one ear. When he's not making soup, he's lifting weights at the gym. He works out religiously. He actually lives out on a farm in the country with his Estonian wife and son. Local people whisper about a strange black man they have seen plowing the muddy fields of this swampy terrain. They think it's a ghost or a mirage.

At night, Ebo reads books about the history of his tribe, the Ashanti. The Ashanti people are fighters, he says. They have never been conquered, and so he will never be conquered either, not even by these pesky Estonians. Ebo likes to tell us stories about his home country. He says there is a village on the coast of Ghana where a shipment of cocaine once washed up after a wreck. The old ladies didn't know what to do with it, so they used it as a powder to stay dry, as is the custom in Ghana.

"They love it," Ebo says. "They dab it here and there after taking a shower. They say it helps them to relax." They also use the white powder as a solvent for cleaning their bathrooms. Then one day, some of Ebo's acquaintances, a pair of shoe-shiners from Accra, the Ghanaian capital, came down to the coast to shine some shoes. They were kneeling there, shining away, when someone gave them some white powder to use to polish the leather. One of the boys sniffed the powder and understood what a fortune they had stumbled into. "Do you mind if we take some of this back with us?" They asked the old ladies. "Sure! Take as much as you want!"

"I felt so good for those boys," says Ebo. "They had nothing. With that powder, they were able to get a better start in this world, that's for sure. Even more powder has washed up."

Miguel the Portuguese thinks we should go to the village. Just to check it out.

"But how do we even get there?" I ask.

"Simple," says Miguel. "First we drive to my place in Portugal. Then we drive to Ghana."

We decide to go to the village.

"BUT WHERE IS YOUR PLACE?"

"One day on my way to write, I encountered a group of Russian sailors. At first, I thought they were extras from the theater, or going to a costume party. But they were not joking. It turned out they were real Russian sailors, and all of them were stinking drunk."
(From my journal, 2018.)

To be a good writer requires consistency, routine. This much has been handed down by the greats. You have to be like Paavo or Jaak. You have to write every day. You have to reach your objectives. Yet this is taxing too. It's hard on your mind, hard on your body. All of that sitting, all of those coffees. The disruptions too, the people who pop into the cafes and stop you in the middle of a sentence. They offer an endless supply of material, ideas, insights, dialogue.

I'm not the kind of writer who can just shut himself off from the world. I need people around me to flow. I need little incidents, conversations. I like the routine of coming up Mouse Street in the mornings to my corner table at the Kringel, the sight of the servers lined up behind the counter in their dark dresses waiting to take my order. I like how the one I like, the dark-haired one who lives in Männimäe and has a boyfriend, leans over and asks me how my coffee tastes each day.

Kuidas maitses?

She's really the most beautiful girl but *mis siis*, so what? There is nothing to be done about it. I am sure that sooner or later she will disappear to some other continent. But she can still be a muse. She can inspire. Almost everything in Viljandi this autumn is filtered through my camera eye. I am becoming a new kind of man here, a real writer. My feelings are all processed through this prism of writing now. There's a set of old ladies who gather on the stoop at the corner of Posti and Lossi streets to swap stories. I encounter them each morning on my way to the Kringel. Not one of them is actually from Viljandi – they were all given orders in the Soviet time to report here for duty as nurses at the psychiatric clinic, or landed a gig as a secretary at the pillow factory.

I don't understand the nuances of this weird Soviet time when you just got a paper that said, "You must move to Viljandi," and people went happily, as if adulthood was just an extension of grade school. The same way your teacher might send you to fetch something from the main office, they emerged from school in Tallinn or Tartu or wherever, and some Leninist God commanded, "Thou shalt move to Viljandi," and move they did. Yet they enjoyed it. It was like a game. They are cute grannies on the stoop in that crooked house, I think. I like old ladies.

Across the street is the Courthouse, which is its own special scene all together. This house is a period piece, circa 1895. All pink and white – it looks like an elaborate wedding cake. There you get to see the local rich boys on court days, who show up in automobiles that no Viljandier could ever really dream of buying. Big shiny cars line up, and their drivers stand around in their finest attire smoking outside. One must have a good smoke before he meets the judge. "Yes, your honor. No, your honor." It's funny, I think. Don't they know that showing up looking like the Al Capones of Viljandi County only makes them look *more* like criminals?

All of these colorful details are captured by my camera eye as I walk the town's streets.

I'm not always in town though. Sometimes Hedvig, the jazz singer, takes me out on excursions. She is a *maatüdruk*, a country girl, from Tõrva. She always has the right clothes for these country adventures. Gloves, shawl, hat, rubber *kummikud* (boots), chapstick (for chapped lips), a thermos of hot tea, some nuts and worm-eaten apples for subsistence piled up in the back seat. I come just like I am, *niisama*, with my city clothes and city shoes. This is a source of great entertainment.

"Oh, ha, ha, ha, *sellised kingad*, those kinds of shoes ...?"

Or, "*Aga kus su sall on?* But where is your scarf?"

I'm so ill-prepared. She takes me to places with weird names. She has scouted up all the good hiking trails around Viljandi. One is called *Varesemäed*, or the Crow Hills. Then there is *Põrgu*, "Hell," a sandy cliff in the middle of Loodi Park. Nearby, on the other side of the park, you can also find the remnants of an old railway that once connected Pärnu and Viljandi long ago. This is where she comes to disappear into the birches. The trees, the landscapes, give her some kind of deep comfort. She's a country girl, as I said. She likes to take pictures of trees.

"But where is your place? Where do you go?" she asks on these sojourns.

"I am actually a port person," I say. "I grew up by the sea. My natural place is in a harbor somewhere, at some seaside eatery, listening to sailor's stories, drinking coffee, enjoying life ..."

"You will need to return to the sea then," she says. "You have to be in your right place."

"But if I squint at Lake Viljandi, then I pretend that it actually *is* the sea. Where the lake ends, I imagine the water goes on, as far as you can reach the ocean. Viljandi is my seaport."

"Maybe so. But it won't last forever. A boy from the harbor needs to go back to the harbor," says Hedvig. "That's the only true way you'll ever find any inner peace. Go to the sea!"

"Not now," I say. "But maybe someday yes. Maybe someday I will go back there."

"Here, look," she takes me by the arm. "Look at that tree."

This is an old oak. It looks like part of it has been shattered by lightning or a storm, but out of this old broken part, a new tree has grown up, a flourishing new branch, covered with red autumn leaves. "You see," she says. "This tree is like us. We have also been broken. But we also have the potential to grow from our catastrophes. Like this tree, we can sprout new branches."

I stop to admire the tree. She takes many photos of it. I've never fully understood her, you know. I don't understand her fascination with nature, her need to be a recluse, to disappear into the woods, or even what the woods give her. We walk out across the meadows on elevated trails in the fog. I feel even more that I don't understand this special Estonian trait which I'd describe as "Fred Jüssi the Naturalist" phenomenon, where people can disappear into the forests like the great Mr. Jüssi and find meaning. I yearn to be back by the seaside somewhere, surrounded by uncouth characters.

Like the Chef, but manifold.

"I'm not of this land," I tell her. "I'm like a lost Greek sailor. I'm just passing through."

"You're a real lunatic, you know that?"

I'm the lunatic? She's the one who's obsessed with trees.

GENERAL LY

"What is real cannot be unreal."
(Lord Krishna, the Bhagavad Gita, 2nd Century BCE.)

On fall nights I try to keep myself busy with back yoga, or *seljajooga*, under the instruction of the great instructor Ly who has returned from a resort on Gili Meno, a tropical island off the coast of Bali in Indonesia. She was working there until an earthquake struck, shattering the hotel and sending lizards scurrying from its cracked walls. When she left for Bali, I quit yoga, but when she came back, I started coming back again. Ly is a small woman, but she marches around like a victorious general.

She surveys her students with an eagle's eye – the room on the second floor of the Mainor Building is now crowded. She steps among her pupils, and then will pull on an arm or a leg. Sometimes she distributes tennis balls. We apply these to our sorest spots. Sometimes we have to put the tennis balls on the insides of our hips, where our ovaries might be. If we all had ovaries.

"You feel that pain?" says General Ly, patrolling around. "That's how women feel during their periods!" There's a lot of discussion then about finding the right spot. I've found it for sure. There is usually only one other man in here with me – Riho, a cheerful older guy who comes to yoga every night. He takes the pain with a sense of great humor. There used to be another man, the one they called *Juuksur*, or the Hairdresser, because he once offered to dye Ly's hair. He was a younger kid with the chiseled face of an actor.

The Chef was certain that Juuksur and Ly were having an affair, because of his handsome appearance. Sometimes they could be spotted eating porridge together at the cafe. Juuksur said he came from Suure-Jaani, but Ly said he's actually a Viljandier. Although recently I haven't seen Juuksur. I ran into him once on the train to Tallinn and he told me he had eloped with a Norwegian girl, and had then made a fortune dealing in cryptocurrencies. I wasn't sure if it was true. I think our friend Juuksur might have been a liar.

Kristiina is my neighbor on the mat. She is slender and has a wonderful golden ponytail. I love watching her stretch out – this might be my chief entertainment in yoga. I love watching it because it seems like such a miracle that a human body can even do such things. Mine can't yet. I feel as if I have known Kristiina all my life, that maybe we went to school together and ignored each other, but now we are at last in a place where we are forced to speak sometimes. She smiles at me as the tennis ball does the same thing to her that it does to me and grunts and I smile back.

"But in life if it doesn't hurt," she says to me, "then it's not worth it."

As each yoga class comes to an end we meditate a bit in silence, and then rise to greet our general Ly with one last *namaste*. Then Ly takes me aside and asks, "Why haven't you been coming more?"

"I've been so tired," I say.

"Why are you so tired?"

"I don't know. I just am."

"You're depressed, that's why. You need female energy in your life. *Naisteenergia.*"

"But where do I get it?"

General Ly laughs and throws out her arms and hugs me.

I think Ly is an artist too. She is an artist with her body. She works herself vigorously. If she doesn't do yoga for a day, she says she feels awful. She wilts, and she falls into lethargy and despair. Her apartment is decorated with winking Krishnas and pictures of Indian chiefs. When she is not stretching, she is drawing portraits in pencil. She cleans obsessively. Ly is my age, and I watch her sometimes. I wonder if she feels about her life the same way I feel about mine.

She married young, to a Japanese man, and they are still together in some way, though he remained in Indonesia. All this global mess, spread around between us, distributed equally from heart to heart. At night, from the misty streets, I can see her sometimes through her second-floor window. Ly is lighting candles and you can see the light of the candles on her face. She has very fair hair and very fair skin, and so is all white-lightness in the window as she lights the candles.

There is an intensity in these quiet moments that you never witness in her lessons where she has a punchy, military energy. Tomorrow General Ly will awake and stretch her body and I will return to the Golden Kringel and start again. Maybe I will even write fiction. Tomorrow, tomorrow. She lowers one of the curtains, looks out the window as if she sees something, but not down at me, and then lowers the second one. The candles are still flickering inside. Oh, this life.

This funny, funny life.

THE SCENE AT UGALA

*Did you know that before the Second World War, Vil-
jandi was known as the City of Kama? Many other
Estonian towns had similar nicknames. Tallinn is still
known as the City of Sprats. But Viljandi was the City of
Kama because Mulgimaa produced so many grains, and
because there was a kama factory in town.*
(Viljandi-born playwright Liis Aedmaa in conversation.)

I decide to take on some side work as a translator at Ugala too,
this grand theater that anchors down one part of Viljandi. Not
long ago, it was actually the border of Viljandi, and the houses
that lie just beyond the traffic circle – called Kantreküla –
were a real village, separate from Viljandi. Those days, when
Kantreküla was its own little *agul* or shanty town, have long since
passed, but the mental barriers remain. Whenever we drive past
Ugala on the hill – which to me looks like a cross between some
kind of North Korean Communist Party headquarters and an
Aztec temple – the Chef will say, "Now we're back in Viljandi!"
out of relief. You get used to being in town here.

You don't want to leave.

My real reason for taking on the translation work isn't the
money though – it's to get close to these so-called theater
people I have heard so much about. Outsiders call them "the
actors" or even *ugalalased*. Within Viljandi, they form their
own social system, with only periodic moments of overlap.
There are theater people and there are folk musicians. There

are the *ossid* who congregate at an underground nightclub called *auk* or "hole" on weekends, and there are the hipsters over at the VLND Villa in the Ingrian House eating those award-winning VLND Burgers. They are eating their VLND burgers as I toil with my own craft. I do not belong among the actors, but as a writer I don't really belong anywhere, maybe only sipping coffee with the likes of Jaak and Paavo.

At the Ugala Cafe, a modern-feeling, freshly renovated place on the second floor, I sit in the corner, trying to translate Liis Aedmaa's play, Mother's Day, *Emadepäev*, and watching the actors and playwrights come and go. I observe, and try to write about them.

I keep thinking something big will happen at the Ugala Cafe, something dramatic, but it's pretty boring up there. It has a nice view of St. Paul's Church on the hill and along the road leading out of town. With some white on the ground from the November frosts, it's all quite pretty.

Sometimes the theater director or one of the better-known actors might come up and order a salad. That is kind of exciting. Other times, some other mildly famous person might stop in for a coffee or two. Liis comes too sometimes. Only my friend Maaker the guitarist is here to keep me company on my Ugala days, along with his new girlfriend. They eat their salads and soups in peace, and I try to transcribe the play but with limited success.

After a few attempts, I just stop going to Ugala.

"All the actors get their drama out on stage," Maaker explains. "This is a quiet place."

There are, of course, the wild parties at Ugala, which everyone in Viljandi attends. Simon the Engineer shows up in his leather jacket and has fun, even though he continues to threaten to leave this "turd of a town," as he calls Viljandi, every other day.

All the Waldorf School parents come to the parties, and once, I even saw Kaja Kallas the politician there. Even the Chef and Musi come. Kaire Vilgats the singer stands on stage backed by a jazz group singing "It's Raining Men," and the old people dance. I try to enjoy these Ugala parties. If I drink, I do on occasion. Sometimes the Chef tries to get me to talk to women at the parties. He's tired of hearing about the Designer and Miss Cloud. "What about those women over there? They look pretty foxy."

It's three ladies from Abja-Paluoja in their Ugala party finest. High heels. Plenty of makeup or *meik*. They sip from fruity drinks or champagne. They welcome my company and I talk to them. Yet there is an empty feeling in the experience. I don't know what's wrong with me.

I'm uninspired and I don't think I can love anymore. That part of me feels dead.

One night, the Chef and the others drag me out to see a play at Ugala. During intermission, we sip bubbly prosecco in the basement cafe of the theater, which is lit up with white panel wall lights, giving it a cosmic, futuristic feel. The clients at the bar are dressed well. High heels, men in black jackets, and one even has a scalplock and some old-school get-up with coat-tails. Our seats are next to Mayor Timpson, a polite fellow who is recognizable because he carpet-bombed Viljandi with YouTube commercials during the election, and we still have some free pencils floating around with his name on them, along with that squirrel that symbolizes the Reform Party. But he won, you know. I hold nothing against him for it. The pencils are also useful.

During intermission, we sit as a quartet at a table. The Chef guzzles more prosecco. The Confectioner from Ormisson is my date and Musi is here. The light from the wall reflects through our glasses. The real conversation is between me and the Chef as we talk about reality and try to deconstruct reality. "But what is real?" asks the Chef. "What is really real?" I don't mind the conversation. There is something very Viljandi about it.

It's staying awake during the performances that's tough. It's just so dark in Ugala, so dark and so warm, and everyone is murmuring away in Estonian. Murmuring and whispering away. Something about a tunnel to Europe. Something. How could you *not* fall asleep there?

The Confectioner has to nudge me so I don't drool on Timpson. This is how I redeem myself in Viljandi. By not drooling on the mayor.

"BUT ONE DAY WE CAN MARRY"

"Hanson testified that she was awakened by the sound of her neighbor's tractor driving towards her house in the middle of the night. When Hanson yelled out the window to the man, to ask what he was doing, the arsonist responded that he intended to burn down the house with her inside."
(Eda Kivisild, Sakala newspaper, 2018.)

Coming down Posti Street on a gloomy December day, I see a blue-and-white police van in front of the courthouse and an older man in a flannel shirt exiting its back in handcuffs.

This, as I learn later from reading the morning's *Sakala*, was a man named Aivar, a neighbor of the singer Hedvig's from Tuhalaane. Aivar was accused of setting fire to her house in the summer. The man's defense was that Hedvig had tried to set fire to her own house. Aivar said she was a witch and he called the charges against him "total bullshit." This was at a time when Hedvig had actually decided to put the house on the market. When I go to visit the singer one day to inquire about the incident, she shows me the damage. Then she launches into a soliloquy about men, women, and love, her most cherished topics. "Love, you see, is not this romantic illusion. Love is actually a process. That's real love. Everything else is just an illusion."

It's as if a neighbor trying to burn your house down is a normal occurrence.

Something that just happens.

"*See on elu Eestimaal,*" Hedvig says about it. "This is life in Estonia. If it's not some Aivar trying to burn down your house, then it's Tiit. If it isn't Tiit, then it's Indrek." She goes on. Then she starts to sing.

"Justin Petrone!" Teet, the famous TV producer and host strides into Restoran Ormisson on a Thursday morning. "Every time I see you here in Viljandi, you are sitting at a table writing!"

Teet looks around at the half-empty restaurant, and then at the girls behind the bar. He has on a black coat, a fine scarf, and his blond hair is perfectly combed as always. He is a television man and he has been a television man for so long that he seems to bring television with him. Even if there is no camera, when Teet the TV producer speaks, he has the perfect intonation of the talk show host, and you start to look around to see if you might actually be on a TV program, and not realize it. This is why I am watching the door to the toilet at Ormisson warily, wondering if Teet's TV sidekick Kristjan will appear at any moment in a tuxedo with both arms extended.

(*Cue studio audience applause!*)

(*Camera One on Teet. Camera Two on Kristjan.*)

(*Action!*)

Teet orders a coffee from the bar at Ormisson and looks around.

"It really doesn't matter what cafe it is, if I am there, you are there writing."

"But that's what I do," I say. "I'm a writer. I write."

Mr. Teet seems preoccupied. He is his usual self, but there is something behind the smile. A troubled gleam in his eyes. I look at him and he looks back. We look at each other again.

"Sometimes I read about you in *Kroonika*," I tell Teet. "When I am missing you."

"Of course," he says, now sipping his cup with a smile. "Of course, you miss me."

"But do you ever read those tabloid articles about yourself, Teet?"

"No," he shakes his head. "Not really."

"Me neither," I say. "They are like articles about someone else."

"Which ones? The ones about me?"

"No, the ones about me."

He squints at me. Teet has appeared in many more tabloid articles than I ever have.

"I don't recognize myself in the articles that have been about me."

Teet gives me another odd look. Maybe he and that Kristjan fellow don't have these kinds of conversations when they have their exotic catered lunches at the *Telemaja* in Tallinn. I forget what Tallinn people talk about. Whenever I go there, I feel as if I have been teleported to another universe, where everyone is happy, beautiful, and rich and sleeping with each other. In Viljandi, everyone is also sleeping together, but they are less happy, less beautiful, and less rich.

"Well, do you think those articles are about you, or just someone who looks like you?"

"I think those articles about me are about me."

"Yes, but it's like fiction."

"How so?"

"It only *looks* real. Maybe it's a real photo, real facts, but the way it's arranged ..."

Teet smiles and takes another swig of his coffee. Again, he drums his fingers on the countertop. The women behind the counter stand stiff-backed, waiting to cater to his every desire. It's not every day that a TV man is here. Sometimes the Reform Party or Social Democrats will have a confab at Ormisson and gorge themselves at the buffet, but that's about it.

Teet is friendly enough, but something is going on within. My madness is explainable. I live in Viljandi. For someone who is known for being carefree, a happy-go-lucky host, he seems tense. His head sort of bobs back and forth. He keeps smiling through it, but something is definitely up.

"But do you really feel that it's you in the pictures?" I press on.

"What do you mean?"

"Do you feel like it's you or someone else? Or, are you the same person?"

"Yes," says Teet. "I can confirm that me and the man in the pictures are the same."

"But the man in the pictures wears a bowtie."

"Good to see you again," says Teet. He winks to me and soon he's out the door.

Again, I start to think I have lost my mind, but then Köler storms in right after him. If you ever needed a metric for your sanity, the eccentric old man in the green hat is it. Köler swaggers up to the reticent women at the bar, barks an order, then turns to me. I look at the man wearily, with as much apprehension as Teet just had for me. He grins down at me. Squints.

Yet I'm actually happy to see Köler. Tallinn has left the building. Viljandi has returned.

"Greetings to our national writer!" Köler proclaims. "What's one of you Italian Mussolini people doing here? Don't you know you are out of place? Some kind of invasive species?"

"Don't you know that I specifically come here to the Golden Kringel because you're not here? I've been trying to work here. If it's not you, then it's someone else. Nobody lets me work!"

"God, what a rip-off," Köler grumbles and ignores me. "The sign says 1.50€ for a coffee! But these people made me pay 2€!"

"That discount is only until 10 AM."

"What time is it anyway?"

"11 AM."

"How was I supposed to know?"

"Don't you have a watch? Or a phone?"

"I only operate on Finno-Ugric time," Köler says.

I again encounter Köler at the end of Tartu Street on a frozen December day, just before Christmas. He likes to mill about in front of his construction site waiting for his victims to pass.

Then he'll rope them in with his peculiar tales. This time though, I don't just get the stories. I am even permitted to visit his workshop. So, this is what the crazy old man has been up to all this time? *And he has assistants?* The elves are very busy in Köler's Christmas Workshop. Busy!

You can see them painting and sawing through the windows. You enter from the street, and soon you will see a sign, *Õhutsoon* ("Danger Zone") affixed to a fence. Outside the building, Köler has jury-rigged some contraption for vacuuming out the pigeon fecal dust that accumulates in the attics of old buildings. He's resurfaced the entire back lot behind the house with this white fluff.

"Park Hotell used it during the renovation," he boasts as he shows me the giant vacuum which stands two-storeys high. "You can't even imagine how much pigeon shit was up there!"

In the yard, wooden planks are stacked according to age. Everything will be recycled, he says. Inside, the elves are toiling away, fashioning windows. Köler's elves are industrious. Our man Köler has used some old sheetrock to create a new kind of wall plaster. He is very proud of this innovation too. Viljandi's Willy Wonka keeps a cot in the back room where he sleeps. His workshop is also his home. Books line the side of the bed, one of which is an old paperback of Herman Hesse's *Siddhartha*. He hangs his hat on the bed post. There's a toilet in the corner.

I'm still not sure what the workshop is for but Köler assures me he's staying on.

"We do not *move* from here," he says. "We *grow* from here. Everything we do here we can do elsewhere. This is just the start of it, boy. You'll see. From Viljandi, we go to the world! From Viljandi to the world!" He fumbles for a cigarette and at last lights it, taking a deep drag.

He is organizing some kind of business, which is as much a lifestyle as it is a business. The refashioning, the repurposing of old buildings. He sucks out the old pigeon dust, makes it new again. Maybe one day Köler will rule Viljandi. There will be a statue in the park next to the one of the real Köler. The whole town is full of such ruins waiting to be saved by such a genius.

The Green House Cafe on these pre-Christmas days smells of warm banana bread, of buckwheat gingerbread, of macchiatos, *tume röst*. Simon the Engineer left Viljandi a day or two ago, completely vanquished, vowing never ever to return. "I'm leaving tomorrow forever, mate," he said. "And I'm not ever coming back. Never!" It was a shame to see a man crack like that, but crack he did. He's put off by nearly everything here. The unimmunized kids at the school, the stern lady at the library who scolded his daughters for doing cartwheels in the library.

Simon is troubled, but I understand his trouble. I used to be the same. Ornery. Miserable. Yet somehow, I've found a way to flourish here in Viljandi. Sometimes I have to eat *maca* and disappear for a while to Ugala, or the Kringel, but I can get by. The second you achieve any peace in this universe, nature conspires to tear it down, you know that. It sends out its hurricanes. There can be no avoidance of catastrophes. After the storms hit, we just gather up our things, and we keep moving forward.

Take it easy. Take it as it comes. Write it all down.

As I write this, Emma, that fun-loving, barrel-of-monkeys youth, stumbles in the door with a wool hat (from Sweden, she says) and a painting easel, because why wouldn't she have one? "But Justin," she says, looking around. "Have you seen Simon? Where did he go?"

"He left a few days ago," I tell her. "He said he was leaving tomorrow, forever."

"Bah! He always says that! You know he'll be back."

Emma is the daughter of Mr. Aivar and Merit the Lioness. She is fearless and joyous. She has a plan that one day she might marry Enn and also help him to run the cafe. The fact that he is almost 60 years older than her is of no consequence. If that plan does not work, her Plan B is to marry me, and we'll run this cafe together. By that time, I will be as old as Enn is now. Either way, she would like to stay here, for she cannot imagine a world without the cafe, and even asks me now and then, "What was life like in Viljandi before the Green House Cafe?"

I tell her Viljandi was a very bleak and desolate place.

"But one day we can marry," she says. "Then we can run the cafe together."

"How old are you again?"

"What does it matter?"

"What year were you born?"

She tells me the year.

"My oldest daughter was born the year after. I changed her diapers. We're not getting married."

"So. That doesn't mean ..."

"Yes, it does."

"Then just pretend I'm older," she says. "Just pretend I'm 20!"

"That doesn't change much."

"You'll see. You and I will marry and Simon will come back."

There's something so sweet about this kid. At least someone wants to be married to me, even if it's some 16-year-old painter with a crazy gleam in her eye who never stops smiling.

"But why do you think he left?" she asks now. "Simon?"

"It takes time to adapt," I say. "It's like those poor British explorers who went to the South Pole and tried to bring tea cups along. They wanted to bring civilization to the South Pole, but it didn't work, so they froze to death in their tents. It was the Norwegians who learned how to use dog sleds from the Inuit who survived. They survived because they learned to adapt. We are not from here, but we have to change ourselves to adapt to this life. Otherwise, we will perish."

Emma looks back at me in a daze. "Wait. I'm sorry, I was thinking about something else. What is it you were saying about the sled-dogs? That was kind of cool!"

"What are you two love birds talking about anyway?" says Enn striding over to the table.

"She wants to marry me," I tell him. "When I'm your age. Then we can run the cafe."

"I think it's a great idea," says Emma.

"Ha! *You*? Run *my* cafe?"

"That's her plan."

"No, no, no. No, no, no. No writer bum like you could ever run a successful cafe."

"Why not?"

"Because," he huffs, "you haven't got the smarts."

MONK STREET

"His soul swooned slowly as he heard the snow falling faintly through the universe."
(James Joyce (1882–1941), "The Dead", 1914.)

We left fifteen minutes before the hour, the last time we would leave the house that year. My youngest child was bundled in her winter outerwear and hoisted on my shoulders. Fireworks crackled and exploded from back alleyways and dim streets in the Old Town. Then somewhere there in the distance above the noise, I could make out a familiar, scratchy voice crooning like crazy above it all. There was a blare of a trombone and a lazy rhythm slinking underneath.

Others were moving toward the sounds, swaddled clumps of four or six, navigating the ice-chunked sidewalks to Turu Street and the *hoov* of Vilma, one of the buildings of the Academy. I call it "the carrot house" because one of its pillars is painted orange like a carrot. There used to be a pastry business here. Before that, there was a windmill.

"Where are we going, Daddy?"

"We're going to the carrot house."

It was a slippery walk into the *hoov*. We were engulfed by people waving tiny blue, black, and white flags. There were hundreds of characters packed into that little industrial space. The silver tanks of the old pastry factory reflected light down onto the cold huddled masses.

"*Head vana aasta lõppu,*" I heard a few say to each other, but mostly they were content to watch. Ruslan Trochinskyi and the rest of his band Svjata Vatra serenaded the onlookers with vigor, and now more than ever, with his mohawk frozen in place, he cut the figure of a dashing rooster, while he blasted us with more trombone.

Ruslan seemed more confident than he had when I had first seen Svjata Vatra many years ago. Back then, he was more of a young upstart. He had something to prove by holding a scythe above his head and crying out bare-chested, *"Oh, I want you. I want you so bad, baby."* Now his performance was slick, fluid. He rolled off the other musicians, his delivery was tight, and he sang with gusto. Ruslan was actually getting better with time. All our lives we were told that youth was to be the best time of our lives. Told that this was the time when we would do our best work, be our best selves, make our best music, and also look better than we ever would again.

Everyone followed this trajectory from bright flaming youth to mediocre middle age, where one became a mere reflection of an earlier self. But it just wasn't true. Ruslan was getting better and I knew I was getting better. I had come here one night on a train alone, yet now I was surrounded by friends. I had no discipline as a writer before. Here I have become a writing machine, producing columns and articles for magazines. I have become like Jaak the Diplomat, "writing constantly". Churning it out. The next great feat would be no doubt, as Paavo had said, to write a novel. I was moving forward, like Ruslan. The only way for us now was up, forward, *edasi*.

Everything that had happened up to this point had been an audition. The greatest events had not yet taken place.

There were so many Viljandiers I didn't know in the crowd. In fact, other than Ruslan, I didn't see anyone I recognized. This wasn't because my friends weren't there. It was because there were so many Viljandiers I didn't know. They were here and Ruslan was singing, "Kalyna."

"Daddy, don't look at those people." My youngest child gripped my head and forced it to face the stage. My youngest daughter Maria was seven, and could still sit on my shoulders. She had come to visit me.

"Watch the musicians!" she said. "See that man who looks like a rooster? Watch how he plays!"

Earlier that evening, I had finished refueling the fires in the furnaces and closed them. I removed the clothes out of the washing machine and set them out to dry.

While I was touching the laundry, something happened though. I looked around, made sure the curtains were drawn, and there was not one opening through which someone could see what was about to take place. Then I went into the bedroom, curled up in the bed beneath a blanket and began to sob. It was a deep, heavy cry.

There were plenty of good reasons to do it but I didn't really know what had caused it. The repetitiveness of wood furnace heating? The dampness of a child's wet socks? How could it happen? How could a grown man just break down crying? Why?

The thing was that I hadn't cried in years. I hadn't cried at any funeral. Nothing could bring me to tears. I was rock solid. Yet here I was, curled up in a bed sobbing all alone on New Year's Eve. When it was done, I got up, washed my face, and went to get the child ready for the concert as if nothing had happened.

As the last metallic notes of Ruslan's trombone tinkle into the sky, Kangilaski the illustrator approaches me and invites us to the Old Water Tower to watch the fireworks. With Maria still on my shoulders, we trek across town. A small crowd gathers at the foot of the tower. Laineli arrives at about seven minutes to midnight with a feather in her hair, and holding the old iron key. Up we go, around and around.

"This is like the Statue of Liberty," I tell Kangilaski.

"Have you really been there?"

"Of course. You climb up all of those steps. Then you get to the top, look out at New York Harbor for about 30 seconds and climb down. It's more or less the same experience."

At the top of the tower, we survey the town lights, which glow like many lanterns. There are more bursts of fireworks. From above, Viljandi looks like some kind of strange amusement park. There's the Town Hall over there, the lights from Ormisson, the spire of Saint John's, the little cars driving up Kauba Street. There is endless fun to be had down there, endless new experiences. Every day can be the same, and yet it brings something new and different with it.

When the clock chimes, it's over. The sky explodes with sound, light, and fire. Kangilaski approaches me, her mouth shut but arms open, as if she is holding her breath.

"*Head uut aastat!*" I say at once. "Happy New Year!"

"Thank you," she gasps for air. "Happy New Year to you as well. You know that it's very good luck if a man wishes it to you first."

"One should never whistle indoors either. The house might burn."

"You are a true Estonian," Kangilaski says. "Thank you for wishing it to me first."

She seems really pleased, as if she actually thinks she will get extra good luck from it. Kangilaski invites us to a bonfire in one of the yards in the Old Town. The ground has frozen solid following a brief thaw and has turned a lovely purple color. Someone has suspended some Christmas lights from the eaves of a nearby house and they cast golden circles on the ice.

We stand there for a while around the fire as the firework bombardment continues. The yard wasn't far from our old home on Sepa Street, the house where this child, our youngest, was born. It already seemed like ages ago. When she sees the house, she wants a closer look at her birthplace.

The curtains are drawn, but there is light in the house, and we can see into the windows. On one of the window sills, dolls and other toys have been arrayed by some hand. "A girl like me lives here now," the child says. "I wonder who she is. I wonder what her name is."

"Let's come back some day and find out," I say.

We begin to walk back home from our old house on Sepa Street. We bid goodbye to our friends at the bonfire and then turn up Munga or Monk Street. It is named Monk Street because there used to be a monastery here. My face is growing numb from the cold, and my cheeks still feel salty, though I have already forgotten about my emotional outburst earlier. It is as if it had never happened. My emotional breakdown. How do those things even happen? I can imagine crying at a funeral, or maybe a sad movie. But why does a man start crying over wet socks?

"Why do we celebrate tonight anyway, Daddy?" Maria asks.

"Because it's a new year. Isn't that a good reason to celebrate?"

"So what if it's a new year?" she scoffs. "It's just some numbers anyway."

"People believe a new number brings new hopes with it. New possibilities."

At the end of Monk Street, a solitary figure stands facing us. The figure wears a long-striped coat and a hood is pulled over its head. The lamp shines on the figure ahead, and something silvery sparkles on this person's face. Both hands are fixed on its hourglass hips and from the hips alone, I can tell it is a young woman. She stands there, just waiting. Then she cries out to us.

"Happy new year! *Head uut aastat!*"

When I get closer to her, and can finally see her face beneath the hood, I know exactly who she is. It's a mysterious girl I have seen around town sometimes, the one with the golden locks and freckles. The one with those eyes. I would see them watching me. I had even seen her once, a long time ago, dancing with Emma at some raucous Viljandi party.

"Who is that girl?" I had whispered to a friend. "Just some Viljandi girl," he had said. "See how she dances so freely?"

Her eyes look back at me now. We have seen each other before, but never spoken.

"It's you," I say to the woman, who turns as if to welcome the two of us. "You're ..."

"Yes," she smiles, "I'm ..."

"... but haven't we met? Do we even know each other?"

"I believe we do."

It's a wonderful feeling to stand there in the snow beside her. Somehow, even under the firework bombardment, we are alone here, the three of us. The snow falls faintly down and you can see the thick wet flakes drifting in the lamp light. The young woman squints at me and responds with a very curious smile. Then her eyes light up. Now I can see her freckles and soft curls, and that silvery writing on her cheek. She has written the numbers of the new year.

"Of course, you know who I am," she says. "I'm –," and she tells me her name.

"Of course," I say, removing my hat. Then I touch my face as the horror of it dawns.

"What is it?"

"Oh, no."

"What happened?"

"I'm so sorry."

She steps back. "What did I do? Has something gone wrong? What happened?"

"No, it's just. Well, you're a woman and I'm a man."

"*Nii.*"

"So I was supposed to wish you a happy new year first."

"You were? But why?"

"It's good luck in Estonia if a man wishes it to a woman first."

"How does that work exactly? I've never heard of that."

"You haven't?"

"Never."

"That's just what I've been told. It might not actually be true."

"Who is she, Daddy?" the child asks over the top of my head. "Is she your friend?"

"She is my friend."

The young woman in the hood looks up and smiles and waves to the child.

In the distance, there is another blast of fireworks. We are all getting dusted white by the snowfall.

"Tell you what, though," I say, putting the hat back on my head. "Next year, I will make sure to wish you a happy new year first. We can do it here in Viljandi. Me and you. I promise."

"Oh," she says and blushes. "Oh." Then she puts her fingers to her lips and blows a kiss. My heart stirs when she does it, and something very hard and very icy inside me melts a bit.

We stand for a moment like that, then begin to walk deeper into the town, closer to the lake. Paths have been shoveled through the high snow drifts and we move between them. The child keeps watching the lights and the people and grows quieter and quieter. The lights from the hotel cast a yellow light on the facades. Viljandi is just some small town in Neverland, but it can be very beautiful. My soul swoons from the sight of the lights and the snow. From the spirit of the girl.

"So, where are you headed?" I ask the young lady after some time. "*Kuhu sa suundud?*"

"That's just the thing," she says. "I don't know where I'm going. I haven't got a clue."

"How perfect."

"Why is that?"

"Because I don't know where I'm going either."

THE TIGRESS

"Everything, everything seemed encrusted with portent."
(Annie Proulx (1935–), "The Shipping News", 1993.)

Thrown out of the house at 7 AM by my pre-teen daughter who demands to change in private, because my room is on the way to her room, and she's in a towel. "Please get out, please just leave," everything is in disrepair, the heart as tattered as a war flag. There are piles of dishes unwashed in the sink.

I breathe out into the winter cold, just to watch my existence vanish in the wind. This rudderless, anchorless existence that leads one over ice on streets past peaceful wooden houses, smoke rising from them in cheerful puffs. The wooden crosses carved into the door of the old Orthodox church on Mäe Street bulge like disapproving eyes. I turn down Kraavi toward the Roosi Street Villa, still under construction.

How many times? How many times must I walk this town empty hearted with an empty stomach? Stripped down and stripped bare? The mossy icy stones of the Castle Ruins rise up like the bones of elephants. I just cannot stand this passion within me. It's too big, even for a large manly body. I turn to cross the *Rippsild*, the old Suspension Bridge. I look out at my

"Hills of California" – like cold breasts, I think – and I crave warmth. I need warmth and empathy, but I just stare out at the scenery.

Viljandi is like an elephant graveyard, I think. This is all you get. All you get is some ruined buildings, rotting old bones. But it's not true! By 9 AM the cafe is open and you can get a cappuccino. On the way back to the cafe, I come across an old wall. Someone has written *kalli* ("hug") on it.

A light snow gives way to a blue sky. A plane makes its way across the blue. Nothing is ever over. There is a tide, it flows in and out, but it's never really over.

It comes over me in the shower, as it always does. There I am, standing, the warm water rushing down on me, and then I just feel that pull, that pull of her, the lady from Monk Street. I have become fixed, you see, fixated on the past, fixated on the Designer, fixated on Miss Cloud, but for the first time, I feel someone *new* pulling at me, pulling me over. It's as if a voice is saying, "Hand it over, hand it over." Then, at some point, I let down my guard and I am awash in the warmth. The love-feeling. That's the thing. Naturally, she has to come to the cafe that day.

I'm seated in the corner when she comes in. It's a gray winter morning. The young woman sort of bounds into the cafe, half startled, as if she isn't quite sure she really wants to be in the cafe, or wants to be in Viljandi at all. She peers around and then goes to the counter and places her order.

The young woman of Monk Street has returned. I recognize her by the striped coat she was wearing on New Year's Eve. Her hair is an awesome gold mess. She nods to me and I also acknowledge her existence. Then she takes a seat in the farthest corner of the room. She sits over there and just stares at me, and I look back at her, but say nothing. She quickly rises and bounds past me into the back room of the cafe and takes the farthest seat there.

I glance over my shoulder and see she is sitting there and she looks back at me again. Her cheeks are rosier now, most likely from the cold, and I know then that something must be done about it. So, I walk over to her. There's another young woman in the back room, probably from the Cultural Academy. She sits in the corner studying, but observing us with interest over her book. She looks very, very amused by us.

The first thing the young woman asks me as I sit down is, "But what is your sign? Your *tähtkuju*." She has the most wonderful twinkle in her eyes. A truly bewitching sparkle.

"I am the Scorpion," I say. "This is usually the moment when people get up and move to another table. Everyone thinks we are terrible. It's almost a handicap. People don't like us."

"But I am an Aquarius," she says. "So, I am not afraid of you."

"I like this one, actually. They always have something interesting to say."

"But your year? What animal are you?"

"Oh, I am a sheep. All warm and fluffy." I feel very warm and fluffy.

"Oh?" her cheeks grew even rosier.

"I was married to a tiger for a long time. You know what they say about the tiger and the sheep? Sooner or later, the tiger eats the sheep! That's what happens to us sheep and tigers."

"I am a tiger too," she says and smiles. It's an enchanting, ferocious smile.

"Well," I say to the lady I now call the Tigress. "I suppose we can still be friends."

Just then, the tea arrives in a beautiful ceramic pot. The Tigress removes one of her earrings and places it on the pot. It's the same color of brown-gold and her eyes roll in delight. "Do you see, do you see this earring?" she purrs. "It goes well with the teapot, doesn't it?"

"It does go well with the teapot, yes."

She pours herself a hot cup of the liquid, drinks it up with her paws.

"So," I say. "What do you do? What 's your job?"

"Me? Well, I'm actually an elf. A *päkapikk*."

I eye her in wonder. This is getting better each minute. A tiger *and* an elf?

"That's why I'm here," she says. "I have to wait until the workshop opens."

"I understand. Elves work very hard."

"Yes," she wrinkles her nose. "I am not sure if I am going to stay. Elf work is hard work."

She is very serious about this elf business.

"Where did you go to school? To become an elf? Elf University?"

"But I haven't studied at a university yet. I just got out of high school."

"Wait. How old are you?"

"Twenty."

"Oh. I imagined you were twenty-something. Not twenty-zero."

She shrugs in a carefree way.

"Well," I say, drumming my fingers on the table. "Well, well, well."

"What is it? Is something the matter?"

"No. It's nothing."

It is nothing. Nothing and very much something.

So it comes to pass that a man who is not quite middle-aged can be seen through a frosty window flirting with a woman much younger than him in a Viljandi cafe. A woman who claims to be an elf. A woman who has not yet attended college. I suppose it's all predictable now. Quite predictable. This is what happens to men like me. We hang out in cafes with younger women. Still the love-feeling will not leave me. "Hand it over, hand it over," it whispers.

I hand it over.

It's a lonesome, cold winter. Halfway through February I fall incredibly ill. I have to keep my head elevated so that I can breathe. It takes weeks for the respiratory illness to clear, and then I travel to Brussels in the meantime for a work conference. I want to earn some additional money. I somehow drag myself to a small hotel, and then across the street to the conference center. I rasp and gag through interviews, but I do manage to pull it off, and fly back to Estonia too.

Somehow, I survive. From my hotel room, I look out at those pointy roofs of Brussels at sunrise. That big city is a jumble. So, this is the heart of Europe? It's dirty and smells of croissants. But I am still thinking of the Tigress. This tiny sliver of golden hope. We make plans to meet when I return to Viljandi.

But where to meet? That is the question. We can't meet again at the Green House Cafe. That would be too conspicuous. Ormisson? Not neutral territory. What about Harmoonia? "No way," she says. "Too fancy." Finally, we select the Aida Cafe. It seems like a quiet, anonymous place.

When I get there, she is sitting at a table. I can see her tiger-striped jacket. Her golden hair is pulled back loosely. Below it, she wears a loose turquoise shirt that looks as if it was imported from Nepal, Tibet, or one of those other enlightened mountain countries. It feels wonderful to see her.

It's a miracle she even exists. This world is so punishing and lonely, but there are good people in it. That's it, I think, or better yet, I comprehend now. (*"Hand it over, hand it over"*).

I love her.

It is done.

The Tigress does not speak directly. She speaks in a roundabout way. But even in this roundabout, next-level, Aquarian way, I understand what she says and she means. We have a mutual understanding. She talks about losing herself in other people and retaining a sense of self.

She is worried about her ego. When she talks, her tongue protrudes as if she is trying to taste every idea. I cannot even describe where we go on these adventures. Maybe out into the stratosphere, I suspect.

It's all Viljandi talk. "Viljandi is a place where the rule books of life are stacked up neatly in the fireplace and burned," I tell her. She agrees. Her problem is that she thinks too much. One thought leads to another, which leads to another. "Oh," she gushes when we speak, "I am getting so many new ideas! So *many* new ideas when you talk!"

This young woman is from this town. Her parents are from here. She is not actually an elf, but rather must wear an elf's cap at the cafe where she works. This is what she means by "elf work." The more she talks, the more I realize that I cannot plan anything with her. This just cannot work that way. But there are wavelengths bursting out all over the place, frequencies bouncing back and forth. There is some heavy stuff going on.

Of course, Ruslan, that mohawked court trombonist who performs for presidents and kings and the like, is sitting in the corner having a business meeting. This man who croons half naked with a scythe about sex is actually the epitome of the good family man. I am the divorced one. I'm the scoundrel scallywag. The rogue. The godless man.

"Exactly, you're exactly right," I hear Ruslan say from his important business meeting. His wife Terje is there, and they are talking about important matters. Very important things! Ruslan is running for political office now. There's a giant image of him plastered to the side of his car. I see the car all around Viljandi. Ruslan is going places now. He's going places and I'm on a date with a tiger-elf.

The issue is that I do relish her special tiger-elf company so much. After our face-to-face, we agree to walk into town. All the way down the steps, over the bridge, and into the Old Town. That weird energy buzzes between us again, the same buzz that I felt on New Year's Day on Monk Street, with those cosmic radio signals bouncing off us.

There's a full moon out now and it's a gray witchy day. Kerttu the Photographer pops out of the Lossi Commune. Our Kerttu also seems lost in some kind of dream. We walk together, the three of us, but Kerttu quickly tunes into the strange radio signals and leaves us. She's forgotten the name of the Tigress, though they have met before.

"Why does this happen?!" The Tigress growls. "Why can't anyone remember my name?"

The outburst is endearing. In my single years, I have forgotten the wrath of the tiger. Growl away, Tigress, I think. Growl, growl away, until your ferocious tiger heart is content.

"I mean, I have met that girl so many times, and still, she cannot remember my name!"

"I wouldn't take it so personally," I say. "She's just a bit fluffy. A sheep like me."

Just then, two young men approach the Tigress. Two young men whom she knows. Both of them are in good shape, well dressed. They must be handsome, I think. One of them is apparently Brazilian. "*And, you remember my friend Jorge?*" I hear the Estonian man introduce his tanned friend. Watching them talk, I realize that this is just impossible. It's just impossible. I am not young. I once was, but I no longer am. I can try to pretend that I am young, but I am not. I am not old, but as Miss Cloud once told me, I have already lived my life. "*Sul on elatud elu.*"

When I get home, she has already sent me a message. "You are quite the colorful character," says the Tigress. "But I feel that at this time in our lives, we are on quite different levels and paths." It's true. All of it is true! But that doesn't mean that it doesn't make me sad. At home, I curl up on my couch, head below the window, crushed by the pull of the full moon. It pulls on me so hard.

There are books on the table, books about the Estonian statesman Jaan Tõnisson and the famed general Johan Laidoner, both Viljandimaa boys, but I can't be bothered to look at them. The next morning, my daughter throws me out of the house so she can change her clothes alone. It's that cold morning where I see the plane. Where I come across the graffiti that says *kalli*. Hug.

DID KITZBERG REALLY LIVE HERE?

"I was on Tartu Street when I saw a girl walk by with her head covered by an old-fashioned scarf. She had two tin buckets in her hands, as if she was about to go mushrooming or berry picking. I thought, 'What century is this? Have I gone back in time?'"
(Melinda Maarjalill, a woman who moved to Viljandi from Tallinn.)

It's Saturday morning and Jüri the Singer is sitting in his favorite corner, with his omelet and cappuccino. Jüri always orders a cappuccino. This restorative frothy drink satisfies this man's quiet, thoughtful soul. Without the cup, his voice is but a hoarse croak. With it, Jüri is an angel. His quivering tenor makes old women cry, rouses old men from sleep.

Though he is a singer, his plans today do not involve singing. Rather, he will attend a flute concert in Türi, a railroad crossing town to Viljandi's north. Then there will be a visit to an older relative, after which he'll take in a play.

"But who will you go to the concert with?" I ask, taking a seat at his table.

"*Üksinda,*" is his response. Alone. Although it's one word, Jüri the Singer takes his time enunciating each syllable so that it sounds like a whole sentence, if not poetry. "*Üks-in-da.*"

Alone.

"You can't be sure of that yet, Jüri."

Jüri raises an eyebrow but says nothing.

"Think of all those flute players. I think 90 percent of them are female. It's like going to a congress of librarians. There is no chance you'll leave alone."

"*Noh ...*" he takes a moment to ponder the idea. "*Seda küll.*" ("Well ... Maybe really.")

There is also morning talk of the house, the Posti Street House, where Jüri the Singer once lived. "It's a damn shame they took the sign down from that house," Jüri muses over coffee.

"What sign?"

"Well," a pause. "The sign that said that August Kitzberg used to live there."

"*Kitzberg*?!"

This name is known to most Estonians, no doubt. There is even a statue of the writer August Kitzberg overlooking the hills of Karksi-Nuia inscribed with his years of birth and death (1855–1927), and the high school is named for Kitzberg. He is best known for his work *Libahunt* – "Werewolf" – about an outcast Estonian woman forced to live on the margins of society.

I had never read the play, but the 1968 film adaptation is every bit as haunting as Ingmar Bergman's *The Seventh Seal*. In the opening scene, a woman is whipped in front of a white Lutheran church. August Kitzberg had lived in our house in 1893 and 1894, the years when his books *Koopavana* and *Sauna-Antsu Oma Hobune* were written, as well as his play *Punga Mart ja Uba-Kaarel.*

"He lived there for two years," Jüri remarks. "When he lived in Viljandi."

I feel both hurt and vindicated by this news. Many of my friends live in homes of historical value. They walk the same floors as painters, actors, politicians. As far as I knew, ours had just been some house for laborers, maybe employees of the matchstick or pillow factories. Nameless workmen, only one of whom I knew by name, Marek, because someone had carved the slogans, "*Marek on munn*," and "*Marek on türa*" ("Marek is a dick") on the corridor walls.

"You mean to tell me I have been living in the same house as August Kitzberg, the great writer, and nobody ever bothered to tell me about it!"

"They took the sign down when they did the renovation but never put it back," says Jüri the Singer. "But yes, you have been living in Kitzberg's house. Maybe in the same apartment."

Jõeste and her boyfriend Carl Robert are drinking their macchiatos, and listening to our conversation the whole time. This last comment, though causes Carl Robert to lean in.

"Why do you think it's such a good thing that you've been living in Kitzberg's house?"

"Why wouldn't it be?"

"Try to explain so that I might understand."

"Because it's imbued with his spirit, of course! All of his essence has now been passed on to me by osmosis. It's in the air! Kitzberg was great, and one day I too will be great."

"So, you think you are going to start writing a bunch of boring old bullshit plays that nobody reads because you've been living in Kitzberg's apartment?"

"But he wrote *Libahunt*! He was a genius!"

"Yes, he did, and it was quite good, but he also wrote some boring bullshit plays."

"The fact is," Jüri interjects in a rare moment of assertiveness, "that August Kitzberg used to live in that damn house. It was even once called Kitzberg's house." Jüri says it as if some kind of grave historical wrong needs to be righted. "That house is Kitzberg's house," says Singer Jüri. "They should put the sign back up."

"So, what were you saying about your erotic dreams again?" Carl Robert pushes his glasses up his nose as he leans in to address me. Jõeste is unusually silent today. She sits quietly in the corner, her scarf neatly tied about her neck.

Ever since she met Carl Robert on Tinder a year or so ago, she has been, well, more or less satisfied with her personal life. She usually only speaks of his arrivals or departures. "Carl Robert is coming tomorrow," or "Carl Robert left this morning." Our Carl Robert is wearing his Morrissey t-shirt again. He is a fan of The Smiths. Soon our Jõeste will be no more in Viljandi. She will move to the north to join Carl Robert. We lament it somewhat, but it was inevitable. Some people come and others go. Even Kitzberg left.

"As I was saying, before we started talking about Kitzberg, for me the setting of the erotic dream is far more important than the person. It's about the environment. I have had these kinds of dreams about most women I know. The person is not so important."

"This fine lady for example," he gestures to his true love Jõeste.

"Not recently," I say.

Jõeste blushes and winks at me.

"Not recently," Carl Robert chuckles to himself.

"Where was your most recent dream?" asks Jüri.

"It was in the woods."

"What kind of woods?"

"A birch forest."

"Young or old?"

At this, Carl Robert heaves with laughter. He gestures dramatically with his cup of macchiato, and toys with it more in the air as if it was an old pipe. "Young or old! What a question! Well, now, come on and tell us. How old?"

Jüri's face is now the color of beets. He regains his composure and continues. "The ... trees," he stammers. "The ... birch trees in your dream. Were the ... birch trees young or old?"

I pause to remember the dream. I remember the woman, I remember a train, and then I remember the forest and its birch trees. That birch forest. That was the scene of the surrender.

"They were young birches," I say. "Thin and white."

"Like in my forest," he nods. "Tell you what, one day we can go there."

More laughter from Carl Robert. "What do you two intend to do in the forest?"

"No, no," says Jüri the Singer. "That's not what I meant at all. We can visit my birch forest, but you will have to bring your own woman along."

"As will you. From the flute concert."

"*Seda küll.*"

"Do you even have a woman?" asks Carl Robert. It's a sincere question.

"No," I say, reclining in my seat. "No, I do not. Not anymore."

There is some quiet now. A pause comes over the coffee drinkers as they ponder whether or not they should order another cup. Jüri at last stands and puts on his overcoat to walk to the train station, to catch the train to Türi. Jõeste and Carl Robert return to their cozy, comfortable couple feeling. Their mutual affection.

Bittersweet is my feeling. Bittersweet and disillusionment. I cannot say I have not been offered love in these desperate Viljandi years. I cannot say it has not been served up to me warm on a platter. I never took it to heart though. Many offered, but I never said yes.

I look at Carl Robert and Jõeste, with their frothy cups of macchiato. There is a peace, a contentment in knowing there is someone here. Someone here for you. As for me, I can go into the birches, but would anyone else come with me? I'd like to imagine so, but that hope feels suddenly distant and amorphous. Like an old dream.

When I get home, my landlord Kristina is in the yard raking up leaves. She is busy today as she is on most days, dressed in her work clothes, loose pants, an old jacket, and old knit hat.

She is working every day like this, into the late hours working, but does pause to answer my question.

"Is it true that this was Kitzberg's house?"

"Of course!" she says. "Kitzberg lived downstairs. In my apartment, I think."

"Your apartment? What about my apartment?"

"Your apartment was the kitchen. There used to be a terrace here and the kitchen was behind the terrace. A big, old-fashioned kitchen right there. Then the main house was over there, and then all that over there was fields."

"That's right, there used to be more agriculture in town. I've seen the old photos."

"Fields everywhere. Kitzberg lived in my apartment. Yours was the kitchen."

"Oh well," I say. "Maybe August Kitzberg ate soup in my apartment then."

"You're right. Kitzberg probably ate some soup there."

Kristina reflects on the image of Mr. Kitzberg with his handlebar mustache and pince-nez spectacles leaning over a bowl of hot soup in my apartment. In the kitchen, Kitzberg leans over the soup. His glasses are fogged up. He tastes the soup and looks out the window at the fine day and sees two shadows standing in the yard beyond the terrace. Two shadows. He wipes at his glasses. They vanish.

"Well, that was my moment of procrastination," Kristina says. "Back to work."

"*Jõudu tööle.*"

"*Tarvis, tarvis.*"

It's back to work with the rake.

THE FROTHY DRINK

"Viljandi is a little like Florence. You can smell the roses in the parks, watch the fountains spurting. It's a free, romantic place where people are brave enough to be childish and naive."
(Heldi Ruiso, an event planner from Järvamaa who moved to Viljandi.)

Every town needs this kind of place, where two ladies can share a small corner table by a window and talk. In Viljandi there are dozens of cafes just like this one, but this one is our cafe.

Here our two ladies meet almost every morning at just a few minutes past nine. Heldi orders her latte and Jõeste has the macchiato, *tume röst.* Usually she orders two of the dark roast macchiatos, one after the other, but more often than not, with some space for proper digestion. In the afternoon, she'll have another.

No matter who is the barista, Jõeste gets the client discount. She takes note of who makes her drink, tastes it, evaluates it, and assesses.

"Who is making it this morning?" She shoots a look at the machines and you can see the whites of her eyes. "No. Not *her* again. She uses too much milk." Jõeste is not the type to just gulp down a coffee, no matter the make. No. Our Jõeste rises bravely and confronts the barista with her list of demands. I can never hear these conversations – they are too quiet and subdued – but they get her point. The machines clang, steam, another cup is made. This one is on the house.

If Jõeste is pleased with the outcome, she might compliment the barista. She is not to be feared. Rather, her tastes are respected. She is a connoisseur. Who knows coffee better than her?

Jõeste is small but she carries herself with a Napoleon-like imperiousness. She has a haughty step. She's not a full-blooded Estonian either. Maybe this is the difference. Jõeste's grandmother is a Finn. The *noblesse oblige* of Mannerheim fuses in her blood along with dark macchiato caffeine.

"This ..." she gestures toward an empty cup, "is my luxury. Other people go to the Canaries, to Greece, to Thailand. I get to drink coffee." The second cup arrives. The frothy drink. The first is removed and the second is slid before Jõeste. This is done with aplomb and finesse. The server tries to keep her hands from shaking.

"*Sinu tume macchiato, palun,*" she says. "Your dark roast macchiato."

Jõeste thanks the barista. The white froth of the cup has been drizzled to resemble a heart. These kinds of illustrations in the froth are the barista's way of showing off his or her level of proficiency. Yet they do not guarantee a tasty cup. Jõeste lifts the macchiato. Will she approve?

Will this cup be good enough?

When I am permitted to share the table with Jõeste and Heldi, I flatter them with compliments. "Your hair looks especially nice," I say, or, "Your earrings look nice, not to mention your eyes." I've been told that Soviet people did not exchange such niceties. They were cold and severe, *julm*, and did not even touch. Kaari behind the counter is the expert on these Soviet people from the old days. The way she describes it, people used to just rub elbows or something. Even close relatives. I am not a Soviet person. I am one of these perverted Italians. With me, anything goes.

Sometimes when I'm not looking, Heldi will pinch my butt. Jõeste is a bit softer with me. She gives me a wet kiss on the cheek. The women actually never complement each other's eyes though, I've noticed. They complement a beautiful scarf, or a haircut, but never the eyes.

Jõeste will pull back her chestnut-colored hair to reveal a new set of earrings, dangling silver or gems, which arouse an enthusiastic blush from Heldi, who holds her latte with both hands – it looks enormous in her tiny white fingers – while she slurps up the foam.

Heldi is a cute girl, I think. Girl! She's two years older than me, but she looks like a five-year-old. She has curly hair, full lips, and a child-like mischief dances in her eyes. Their birthday parties couldn't have been more different. Heldi's was loud, with balloons and glitter. Jõeste's had candlelight and New Order was playing on the speakers. Then Jõeste's boyfriend Carl Robert downed a bottle of cognac and passed out. We put some books on him and took photos.

That was just a few days ago.

Often though, I am banished to the corner, so they can have a real conversation. I pretend to write, but I do my best to eavesdrop. The best parts are reduced to a whisper, and sometimes not expressed with words at all, but with a shrug of the shoulders or a glance. I don't think they are talking about me though. I'm a bit clumsy. I'm an open book. Everyone knows everything.

Sometimes when we are alone though, Heldi consoles me. She says it's fine and good I haven't wound up in the arms of the Designer or Miss Cloud or any younger woman here for that matter. I haven't told a soul about the Tigress, as I still wish to have some secrets in Viljandi. Just a few of them.

"Thank heavens you're not with any of them," Heldi says. "Be grateful!"

"Why should I be grateful?"

"What? You really want to be 50 years old and divorced from *two* women instead of one? Have *six* children to look after instead of three? As I said, you should be grateful. Let them go."

"It's rather sad," I say. "Not for me. Just that something like that is unfulfilled."

"I know but it's better that way. It's better. Trust me it is."

"How so?"

"Some things are just better up *here* in your head, and *here* in your heart than in real life."

The next day. I do need sleep, but then there's work. When the doors of the cafe open, I am there, but there's a line already and Alar the brewer from Võrumaa is there manning the machines. Alar is a friendly sort but I am convinced he did something really bad in Võrumaa that led him to eventually seek a quiet new start in Viljandi. Maybe he stole someone's tractor or something.

Heldi is nestled under a shelf in the corner on a very important phone call and there are a few ominous figures around a back table in jackets that say, "Russian Wrestling Team." To top it off, they are playing the Tintura album again. A moment later, I am out the door and away. It is easier to get some writing done at Ormisson, I decide. Until I get a call from an old friend who is back at the Green House, with a few American tourists, who want to see the best sights in the Old Town.

These are real estate agents from the Mountain West – an older couple, who are polite, unassuming types. We only have a bit of time to look around so I take them toward the Castle Ruins but along the way, they notice that little brick house that looks like a religious temple, and the giant painted strawberry plopped in the grass.

"What's that?" the American woman pulls me aside.

"It's the Paul Kondas Centre for Naïve Art," I say. "He was a famous painter, but he had no training. That's why it's called naïve ..."

"We know what naïve art is," the man says. "We even own a few pieces."

We don't make it farther than the center. They devour the place. I know little of art, or art history. I lack the vocabulary to even speak of it, but I am aware that around the corner from our home once lived Paul Kondas, a teacher by profession, who once painted for the fun of it. Or, for the therapy of it. Many of his works have political themes. There is a self-portrait of him wearing Estonian national colors from 1958. Then the famous image of Tallinn getting bombed, that was retitled "Dresden" to pass the scrutiny of any censors. The guests are very impressed with what they see. The man takes off his glasses, toys with them in his mouth and then gestures like an art expert.

"This is all just fantastic," he says.

"Is it?"

"Why, I think it's among the best work we have ever seen anywhere! Definitely, the best."

Kondas's work was exhibited only at the end of his life. In 1979, it was featured in a documentary. He died a few years later at the age of 85. He stayed single throughout his life.

"So, he was a weirdo," I say to the museum curator.

"Excuse me?"

"A recluse. A hermit. An outcast."

"Yes," she nods. "You could say that."

I wonder if my friends from Viljandi had passed the old hermit a long time ago. Perhaps Teet the TV producer marched past Kondas one day in the early 1980s on his way to the beach, but he was probably too focused on getting his next ice cream, or Kelluke soft drink to notice.

"Magnificent," the American man proclaims. "Stupendous. Never seen anything like it!"

Before I leave, I pop a question to the curator. "Why have so many artists thrived in Viljandi? It's a little provincial spot, tucked away from everything. Just some dot on a map. Why?"

"This has to do with the flax," says the curator. "The local farmers made a fortune exporting flax, and this allowed them to send their sons to be educated. With that education, they learned about art and culture, some became artists themselves. That's what I think happened."

So, we owed it all .... to flax. Could there be any other explanation? The water? The air? The strange seaweed growing in the lake that makes everyone itch? There are no explanations.

Just down the street from here, the Golden Kringel glints in the sun. Villem Ormisson the painter was just nine years older than Kondas. They came out of the same milieu, although Ormisson had a more tragic end.

In 1941, with the Soviets crawling all over the country and knowing he would likely be deported because he came from a wealthy family, he committed suicide. That very same year, Paul Kondas arrived in Viljandi as a young school teacher. He lived a few houses away from the Park Hotell Viljandi, and it's very likely that before they shut the hotel for good, young Kondas spent his days just like me, sitting in the corner booth of the hotel restaurant, enjoying a frothy drink, admiring the weather, and trying to sketch out some ideas.

JAAK RETURNS

"If Viljandi still has its own spirit ... One who is every-where and nowhere at once. It gently harasses someone and infects Viljandi with incurable love."
(Lauri Räpp, a writer whose grandmother lived in Viljandi.)

Jaak is a talkative fellow, or can be if the topic interests him. With the springtime weather, he too returns to Viljandi, taking the back table on the terrace, in the corner below the tree. Here, he mostly sits alone, daydreaming over his latte in a pair of shorts, a button-down shirt, and sandals. Sometimes he is joined by his female counterpart, or better half, known as Viivi the Poetess. They sit together and drink. She speaks about one-tenth the amount that Jaak does.

Sometimes Viivi plays tricks on him. In the winter, Viivi told me that Jaak had given up drinking coffee. "Jaak can't stand it anymore," she said. "He says he can't even stand the taste. *Talle enam ei maitse.*"

I later caught them at Karamelli sipping lattes. When I asked Jaak about the rumor he had given up the stuff, Viivi abruptly left to order another round.

"*Me*? Give up *coffee*?" he scoffed. "And Juncker has given up cognac!"

Yesterday, Jaak was alone and I tried to dig some political opinions out of him with limited results. I wanted to know what he thought of the new government, and this provoked a long monologue and multiple references to books about the decline of Western Civilization. "Here, you should read this. It's all here." He tapped at the screen of his well-worn iPad.

Jaak had on a gray shirt that day and a pair of sunglasses. He spoke with authority, clipped, well-formulated sentences. There was a hurriedness to it. A few jabs with his finger in the air, but the arms mostly folded. The concerns that drive voters to the populist parties are real enough, the wise man admitted. They have been there for years yet no one has done enough.

"It's all here, you see. Here, here, and here."

Taavet, the bassist for the folk ensemble Curly Strings, had been sitting nearby trying to enjoy a salad but after about 15 minutes of listening to me and Jaak go back and forth about European politics and writing, he got up and excused himself.

Jaak's heart wasn't in it though. The man is really passionate about the *sirelid* (lilacs) that are blooming all over Viljandi Town. It's May again, and the cats are breeding in the alleyways and yards. One can hear them whining as they mate in the night. The lilacs are in bloom, and their fragrance perfumes every breath. The town has become something of a wonder, a romantic daydream. Mention the lilacs, and Jaak's sunglasses come off at the cafe. He is instantly restored.

This morning, he is seated at his usual table in his colorful summertime attire. Populism, deep states, these are drab gray topics. Mention lilacs and Jaak swings his body around and starts to roll his fingers together as if there was a flower between them. He becomes an old school poet. "Allow me to school you, allow me to enlighten you to the *sireliõnn*, the luck of the lilacs."

Jaak actually smiles now.

"The luck of the lilacs?" I scratch my head.

"The *sireliõnn*," he inhales deeply through his nostrils. "Can't you just smell it, man?"

"I guess so," I sniff at the air. "But where can I find this so-called luck?"

"Where? Why ... *everywhere* of course! But only now, at this time of year. There is a very narrow window of time available. Time is of the essence! You must use this precious time!"

There is a kind of science though to finding, or rather achieving, the bliss of the *sireliõnn*. According to Jaak, most lilac blossoms only have four petals. The trick is to find those with an extraordinary number, with five, or even six petals. Those who find these wonders are imbued with luck, prosperity, but only if you eat them. After one finds the *sireliõnn*, life bubbles like ambrosial champagne. Your manuscripts write themselves. This is the reason for his success as a writer. Flower blossoms!

"And do you know what my record was?" asks Jaak.

"No."

"Go ahead. Guess."

"Seven?"

"FOURTEEN!" he cries. "I've found 14 blossoms! Can you believe it?"

Somehow this is more exciting than the decline and fall of Western civilization.

"My record was 16," says Viivi. She has sat here all this time with her hands in her lap listening to Jaak's explanation of the *sireliōnn*. "This is a tradition that comes from Germany. It represents the German influence in Estonia. The Finns, as far as I know, don't hunt lilacs."

"I think you are right about that," says Jaak. "I don't recall the Finns doing it."

"So, this is what you talk about when you negotiate with the Germans?"

"Of course," the diplomat says. "We talk about all manner of things. All manner of things! There just always must be something to talk about."

"But where can I find the luckiest lilac blossoms, *Härra* Jaak?"

"Just go and find them. Fourteen. *Sixteen*! The Viljandi streets are full of them. *Va bene!*"

With his words in mind, I set out to wander. I come down Mäe Street past the little Orthodox chapel, glancing at it briefly, and then come up and around Liiva Street, a sand and gravel road that isn't even marked on maps. From there, I follow Ranna Street past the mouth of Pikk Street and beyond the ruins of the castle that stands high above, and at times I can see the shadows of men and women high on the castle walls and hear their faraway conversations.

Then I turn up the path that leads into the forest beyond the ruins, a little patch of landscape between the fortifications and the Valuoja stream. This place I call "California" because the green treeless hills remind me of the fertile farm country south of San Francisco. That opening to the woods, the way it leads into a place unseen, has always piqued my curiosity, so I walk in.

Here I get lost in the roll of the hills, the foliage, the big boughs of lilacs hanging down all around me, the soft heft of the blossoms in my palms. They seem so full that it would be impossible to count them all, and so I feel a hundred or a thousand times blessed over, just to be alive, to smell their aroma, to fill my heart with it, to get lost in green. What incredible luck!

I hike up a hill, slide down another. At the crest of another I view the lake from end to end, then decide to go down. The whole forest seems to be alive, everywhere I hear movement and rustling but see nothing actually move, except the ferns that sway in the air. Other than that, everything is silent. It's just me, my memories, and my thoughts. As much as I can stand them.

At the cafe later that day, I take a seat at the back table – Jaak's table – and order my latte and try to write. There is a new young woman working there and her name is Sirel – Lilac. She has straw-colored hair and a wholesome look. She's just 20 years old. That much I already knew. There is a rare honesty to Sirel that sets her apart from the town girls who already looked so jaded and tired. For me, given the instability I have been dealing with on a daily basis in my personal life, conversations with her or Jaak make a big difference.

Viljandi grounds me, gives me peace, I can retreat into it. Kind country girls. Hunting for lilacs. Off-kilter conversations with Jaak. The world around me is slowly going to hell, but Sirel and Jaak and Viivi are here.

When Sirel comes, I ask if she has ever searched for the luck of the lilacs.

The *sireliõnn*.

"Every day," she says, picking up the dishes from another table to take away. "I have to. It's my name."

Coming down Lossi Street later, I see a woman walking alone. It's Viivi, the Poetess. The force that arranges people in certain places has arranged her there at this moment. I walk by her side for a while before she looks up and notices that it's me. She smiles but doesn't seem surprised.

"So," I say to the Poetess after some time. "Have you found the luck of the lilacs yet?"

Viivi smiles up at me. She squints. "I haven't looked," she says. "Have you?"

"Not really."

We walk on together in silence, but it's a comfortable silence. This is not the silence of the woods when I was there alone. This is the silence of the Poetess, the silence of the lilacs.

"So, what happens if you find 16 anyway? Do you get everything you want?"

"Not exactly."

"Then what kind of luck do you get?"

"You get your own kind of luck, I guess. The kind of luck you need."

"I know a woman who searches for them every night. Her name is Sirel."

"She must be very lucky."

"She is."

"But you need luck too."

At last, we arrive at the square. The trees are so green and bewitching they could rival the visions of the impressionists. They move about gracefully in the air, as if speaking tree language.

"They look like something Ormisson would have painted," I say.

"*Kevad*," Viivi says, as she stands watching the trees. "Spring at last."

THE NIGHT OF CAFES

"Last night I saw Simon at the party at Ugala. There were all of these Estonians dancing in the Black Box. Simon said, 'Where am I? Where the bloody hell am I?' And I answered, 'You're sleeping in your dressing room. You're back on tour. Very soon you'll wake up. Viljandi is just a dream. Very soon you'll wake up from Viljandi!" (From my journal, 2019.)

One night, I dreamed of Viljandi. Except that it wasn't the real Viljandi. It was some other kind of Viljandi, assembled from the same elements, but different. The houses were all the same, the terraces and gardens, the wooden shanties built into the sides of hills, with a cold wind blowing through. I crossed streets and back alleys. Most of my dream Viljandi was full of well-trodden footpaths, like the one over on old Kassisaba Street. This is the path that runs alongside the fortifications until you reach the great oak that stands beside the Villa Rosenberg on Pikk Street.

All of it was like that.

Eventually I came upon a small yellow house in the middle of a hollow. The lights in the house were on and so I went in. There was a beautiful blonde woman standing in the kitchen when I entered. The most beautiful woman there ever was. She looked like a Baltic Finnish woman, a *läänemeresoomlanna*.

A big roaring fire was in the wood furnace. She was making a cake by the window, and had on an apron. "I have been

waiting for you," she said. "*Tule siia.*" "Come here." We began
to kiss by the window. It was one of those passionate kisses
where you almost feel you are digging through layers of passion. One layer leads to another, which descends to another.
I reached into her dress and pulled a breast out and began to
suck it. I heard her gasp. You cannot imagine the peace I at last
felt in my soul. I had been so hungry for so long.

"Just wait," she said, stroking my head. "Just a second.
Please, just give me a second!"

The woman in the apron disappeared into another room
and I stood there in the kitchen. What was she doing? I imagined she was getting the bed ready for us with many blankets.
Nice and warm. Or maybe she was taking off that apron of
hers, along with that soft, wonderful dress. A moment later
she emerged with a wooden drawer in one hand and in the
other a screwdriver.

I stepped back. "What's this?"

"Before we make love," she said, "would you help me
assemble some furniture?"

Horror seized up in me. "No," I said. "No. I just can't do
that."

I turned and I ran out the door, back through the hollow,
up the footpaths into my dream Viljandi. I ran and the blonde
woman came running after me with the screwdriver and
drawer.

"Get back here!" she screamed. "Get back now! You have
to work! You have to work!"

"No," I yelled back. "No, I don't have to work."

"Yes, you do! Get back here now and put this cabinet together!"

"Never!"

At last, I reached the dock on the lake, down by the Old Boathouse. I looked back and she was still following me with the screwdriver and drawer, and still yelling. "Get back! Get back and assemble it now!" There was nowhere to turn, nowhere to run to, so I leapt off the dock into what I thought was the water. Yet somehow, I was borne upward into the air. *Was I flying?* I looked down. Yes, it was happening. I was flying now. The woman reached the dock and began to stab at the air with her screwdriver. I pushed harder up into the air. With each push, I went higher and higher upwards. All of Viljandi was just a toy village of building blocks and blinking lights. Away, I thought, I must get away. And there on the dock I could see the woman in the apron screaming.

"Get down here this instant!" she screamed. "You have to work! You have to work!"

"Just look at you," the Chef says after I recount the dream. "This country has traumatized you. You can't even have a sex dream without someone asking you to assemble some furniture here."

It's the Night of Cafes in Viljandi, we are seated around a little table in Romaan. Something has let out, a concert somewhere, something big, because people are pouring into Romaan. The yard is full of young ladies in straw hats and hipster dudes playing table tennis. They are out the door, up the steps, on the broken couches, around the tables. You have to hold your stomach in to move through these crowds. There is a line at the bar, the two bartenders serve the inebriated guests faithfully. The bartenders are tight-lipped, technical types that take no mess. Several glasses of red wine are poured for me. A big glass of Merlot. I choose Merlot. This much I remember.

There is no bouncer at Romaan, there is no guard at the gate checking identity cards. I am not sure if there needs to be one, but Emma – the girl who plans to marry me when she grows up – is seated beside me, all 17 years of herself, enjoying the scene. We have developed a little rapport over the spring, and once we even went down to the lake with my lacrosse sticks and I taught her how to play. She tells me I need to read Jack London. She likes to think of herself as my adviser these days. She hasn't mentioned marrying me and taking over the cafe in a while. Maybe that was yesterday's idea? Or maybe she still thinks it might happen?

"You should read *Martin Eden*," she says. "You should listen to me more. That's what you need. You need someone like me to push you around more, so you can become a better writer."

"Jack London died when he was 40 years old. Maybe I should choose a better hero."

"So? Look at what he produced! He didn't need any more years. He got it all done in 40."

This perhaps sounds like a fortune in time to young Emma. You must appreciate the liberty with which people like her have grown up here in Viljandi. They have grown up with all of these cafes and bars that are willing to at least accommodate them, if not serve them. They enjoy cultural events like this one, the Night of Cafes, *Kohvikuöö*.

All over town, people are operating pop-up cafes out of their homes and gardens. Down by the lake in our friend Peedu's yard, the children run wild and they serve hunks of smoked eel and salad and a creamy cold beet soup. Down there, women in flamenco dresses perform and dance, and little girls also perform for the crowd from the deck. Then Peedu comes out wearing his beret and holding a turntable and starts to play a jazz record. That was earlier then. That was when the people were swarming the streets and hills of Viljandi. The Chef and I got swept up in it and wound up stranded outside of Ave Nahkur's Gallery down the hill. It took us an hour to get back up into town proper. From there we went somewhere else. And like all nights in Viljandi, this one would end here in Romaan.

At Romaan, my heart is sinking a bit. All that blood-red Merlot. The Chef disappears to have his glasses of Tequila Sunrise replenished. Everything is sinking in me. My heart is sinking into my chest, which is sinking into the seat. Emma is talking to me, but I am not following her questions anymore, and this is the sinking moment when a group walks through the door, among them the Tigress in a red dress.

The Tigress.

In a red dress.

It's her.

This rare queen of the animal kingdom.

I am no longer sinking.

No.

I'm completely sunk.

"Oh," is all I can say when I see her. "It's ... you."

There is a gleam of familiarity in the Tigress's eyes when she sees me. Not fear, but not particularly love either.

I can't imagine what it is like for a young woman to be so wanted. Perhaps there is joy in it, a recognition, but it must also be terrifying when the energy is unleashed and starts moving in one certain direction, your direction, because it has to move. This is what happens when I am somehow on my feet and by her side in an instant. This is what happens when my arms are around her and we begin to dance to the music. I can't even understand the mechanics of this thing. Somehow, I am just there.

For almost no part of this vagabond Viljandi life have I ever felt my love fulfilled or respected. It has always been blocked, or redirected, or casually passed over. These Estonian women come and take your heart and then they run away, or tell you that you have no business being with them. Yet once I unite with the Tigress, the radio signals start to hum again. I feel like I am soaring through space. She is still troubled by her Aquarian mind, her interstellar thoughts, but I love her mind and its thoughts.

"My thoughts, my thoughts," she says. "Please don't ask me about my thoughts. My friends tell me, I think too much."

I cannot ask. I can only just hold her for a while. There is something so delicate here that I had forgotten. I realize that I can never judge anyone else for the person they choose to love. These kinds of things just come upon us. I cannot even say that it's me who loves her. I can only say that my soul enjoys her soul's presence. Or something along those lines. I could write and write about it and get nowhere. When the song ends, I kiss her. An image comes to me of a silver kite caught in a wind. If only she could pull down the kite, and calm her cosmic mental energy.

"Thank you for the dance," I say.

"Yes," she says. "But now I must be going."

She bounds over to leave her bag with some friends. Then she's out the door.

I am left with a satisfying ache. This is how it is with the Tigress. She comes and then she goes. I am grateful as I sink into my seat, with my heart full and content. She's oppressed by an overactive mind. My trouble is my moods. When you put these together, you get something very special.

"But who was the girl in the red dress?" asks the Chef.

"Just someone I know."

"You really came alive when you saw her. I've never seen anything quite like it."

I can't remember when the drinking started, but it might have been at one of the cafes behind the old *striptiis* on Tartu Street. We were drinking red wine from plastic cups, although the Chef was partial to his hard liquor. Viljandi on the Night of Cafes is engulfed in a heatwave. All we do is sweat. The Chef with his long hair and beard has started to really look like a Mexican drug lord. He has become a fan of the show *Narcos* and has started using Spanish slang. "*Puta,*" he says. "*Puta, puta!*" And this is how the drinking ends, with a long march from Romaan to the parking lot of Uku Keskus in the early morning dawn, with him muttering Spanish oaths to himself. "*Puta, puta!*" On the way, we meet the perfect specimen of the Viljandi type. A filthy hobo looking for a light.

"Pardon me," he asks in the parking lot outside of Centrum. "But do you have a light?" "*Kas teil tuld on?*"

"What did you say, *puta*?" sneers the Chef.

"*Mul on vaja tuld.* I need a light!"

We look around at each other. None of us smokes.

"None of us smokes, you *puta*. We have no *tuld* for you!"

"Sorry," I say. "We can't help you."

The man grunts and he's on his way.

It's a long hike over to Uku Keskus. The sun is coming up and the Tigress has all but vanished from my consciousness. She leaves marks behind, footprints, but she is also gone into the night. I'm not so sad about it. Not troubled at all. I just enjoy these little fascinating moments. Who knows where she went? Musi has already gone ahead to the car. It's us and our companions. The Chef wanders over to the side of Uku where he finds two *euroalused* (shipping pallets).

He lifts them up with one arm, like a crab. "You can use these in your apartment!" he says. "They will go under your mattress. There's two! Come, give me a hand. Let's take them."

"Put those things down! I'm not carrying that back to my apartment! Are you crazy?"

He drops it immediately, not because he's listening, but because another object has caught his eye. He picks it up and runs over to us. "Do you see? Do you see what I found?" A mad look. "It's a lighter! Go give it to that man! Remember, he was looking for a light? We have a light!"

I think he feels guilty that he called him a *puta*.

"You really want me to go find some drunk guy so that I can light his cigarette?"

"Yes! Don't you see?" he grips my shirt sleeve and looks up into my eyes. "He needed a light, and we have one! That *puta* doesn't need to search anymore!" His eyes are as alive as a child's. This is his nature. He's ready to help. *Abi valmis*. The Chef wants to help a fellow drunk.

"How many Tequila Sunrises did you drink?"

The Chef squints at me as if he is unsure of how to answer, or even what a Tequila Sunrise is, or how that might have anything to do with his discovery. "Look," he says, "it really works."

"We're not going back. You're going home and I'm going home. *Kohvikuöö* is over."

It's not night anymore. The horizon is ablaze with a fiery sun. The birds are chattering.

"Oh," he looks sad. "I'm tired of wearing these damn sandals. So, I'm taking them off. We don't need shoes anyway. This is Viljandi. We don't need shoes. This is the only town in Estonia where you can walk around without shoes on, so take off your shoes. Take off your shoes!"

I obey and take them off, carrying mine in my hand. We reach the parking lot where his ride is already waiting in the car. However, the Chef isn't quite ready to go to the car. Instead, he opens his shorts and urinates on one of the young saplings in the parking lot. He groans in relief as the fluids exit his body. It sounds like a river. At last, he's done, but he still won't get in the car.

"They can just rewind the car to me," he says, arms crossed. "Let them rewind it to me."

"It's 'reverse,' not 'rewind.' You rewind cassettes. You can't rewind a car."

"Rewind the car."

"Let's walk to the car. They're waiting for you."

"I am not walking one step further."

"Let's go now."

"Rewind the car, I said. Rewind it now!"

"You are coming with me." I hook arms with the Chef and escort him to the passenger's side door, open it, and push him in. The Chef looks up at me one last time, pulls out the lighter and lights it again. "It works," he grins as if it is his greatest achievement. "It really works!"

"Goodnight *puta*. Get some sleep." The door is shut and the car roars into the dawn.

This is June in Viljandi. There will also be July and August. The party is only beginning. The Night of Cafes is just the introduction to another hot summer. It's all of that sunlight.

It drives people mad. They do silly things. Too many Tequila Sunrises are drunk, and they start cursing in Spanish. Or, they find themselves dancing in the embrace of a young woman who is too much of a vision to be real.

I'm sure such experiences can be easily had, in any town in this country. I am sure that such experiences can be had, in *any* town in this *world*. For me, these Viljandi experiences have their own mind-bending flavor. They are all pieces of the mosaic, parts of the Viljandi dream.

The next morning, Ebo the Ghanaian and I are walking down Jakobsoni Street. As Ebo is lecturing me about the most impressive moments in the great history of the Ashanti people of Ghana, a young man on an ATV speeds by, with a woman gripping him from behind, her arms wrapped around his waist. This is the kind of vehicle people use in the countryside. The Chef is probably still asleep at home. I haven't heard a word yet. The ATV growls by, displacing the air, and there is wind in the woman's hair. About an hour earlier, I had seen a local motorcyclist riding his bike with the front wheel up, as he went down Koidu Street. He's done this a few times now. He rides around the neighborhood, on just the back wheel. No one pays him any attention. It's just *normaalne*. Normal. For Viljandi, at least.

"It is becoming evident," I remark to Ebo, "that this town has lost its mind."

THE LOVE GENERATION

"For big city people, Viljandi is just some unassuming country place. People are surprised when they hear that Viljandi has its own cinema and a Rimi supermarket."
(Kirke Siimso, "Sakala", 2019.)

The first thing I see when I get back to Viljandi in July is the silhouette of a tramp outside the supermarket emptying his bladder beside a trash can. There is a carefree flagrance to the way he does it, a rogue garishness to it. He just feels about the front of his trousers for the right hole and it's go time, with a loud splatter on the brickwork, puddling up warm in its crevasses.

To my surprise, there's a female tramp waiting for him down the road with a knapsack. She is really waiting, patiently, for her gent to finish. When he does, they're off together, holding hands, out into the not-quite sunset, because it's 11 PM in July and the sun hasn't disappeared.

This is my warm welcome back into Viljandi, although even the locals – and I am a local too – probably don't want to think about the tramps. They just want this place to be known for its views, painted doors, and musician celebrities. Inside the supermarket, a recorded commercial informs me of who speaks for these Viljandi people. *"Greetings, this is Jalmar,"* it begins.

I'm back in the City of Folk.

Up Turu Street, the dream continues. At Layk Cafe, Simon sits quietly in the corner reading Oscar Wilde. Our Simon the Engineer is back in Viljandi, of course. He has his bouts, he hates, he rants, but something keeps him coming back to here. And not only for his daughters.

He's putting together a band that plays the best of British new wave and they are planning to go on tour, playing gigs up and down the Baltics. There are rumors too, that he is also looking around to buy a house. Simon seems incredibly subdued today for a man who used to give me nightmares about killer whales. Maybe he's getting used to the place?

"What news from New York?" he asks.

"New York was great. I was there for a month."

"I can tell. You actually look happy, mate."

He also looks happy. Restful. Content. Maybe his soul has made peace with the town.

In the back of Vilma, the folk ladies are crouched once again over their sprawling masterpieces. Folk patterns are being sewn into mole fencing that stretches across the floor of the back of the woodshop. They use old LPs, CDs, and VHS cassette tape to create the designs. They've been at this for months. This is what is called "upcycling," making something beautiful out of yesterday's trash. The Designer walks from room to room, observing the scene while she nibbles from a massive Donald Trump milk chocolate bar I brought her from the US. Then she crouches herself over a patch of the fencing to sew a red felt flower into place with a ribbon.

In the weeks before the festival, she traveled around the country in search of inspiration, including to Kihnu Island. The pattern being stitched into the mole fencing is a Kihnu pattern. This is what one of the core team tells me, as she ties ribbons to the clothesline with her newborn son dangling from a sling on her chest. I don't bother to ask the Designer about the pattern today. I already know what she will say. "*Olen väsinud ja ma ei viitsi sellest rääkida.* (I'm tired and I don't feel like talking about it.)"

Slowly a heatwave sneaks into town and everyone starts to sweat. The stage is going up on Kaevumägi now, big stacks of pipes, the sound systems are being screwed into place.

The Designer and her vegan sister Pets are sitting down at the Song Festival Grounds as another builder in a hard hat hoists their ribbon decorations up over the back of the stage. I can't say the Designer looks tired, but she is preoccupied. Her sister has adopted a stray dog with a fine coat, like a seal's. The first few days, all it did was bark and drool. Now it comes running and licks my hand.

There are more strange cars in town now, strange people, strange conversations outside my window in the wee hours. Tomorrow it starts. There's apprehension about this thing. I guess there is nothing to fear, or worry about, in all of this folk business, but life will take its course.

On the second morning of Folk, I notice a black lace bra dangling and drying in the sun, from an open window. Who even knows why it's there or how it got wet? Maybe a late-night dip in the lake? But why would anyone swim in a bra and to whom does this particularly black lacy one belong? The Designer? Someone else? Questions about the wet bra abound.

The line at the cafe is out the door. Alar, our mild-mannered barista from Võrumaa, has about two-dozen sticky notes plastered to the espresso machine, scores of orders for light cappuccinos, dark cappuccinos, macchiatos, espressos, Americanos, "but leave plenty of room for (almond) milk."

On the back terrace, a group of fiddlers has taken over. Every table is full and there are empty cups everywhere. It's so hot now. A dog is under the table, panting. A woman in a paisley dress brings the dog a bowl of water, dripping with condensation. The dog laps up the water and the woman drinks her coffee, dreaming away in the sun. A violinist looks at me and then at the dog, and continues to play.

Meantime, our man Enn is in the corner, talking about Woodstock.

"Everyone's always talking about the Love Generation, man. The Love Generation, the Love Generation. Bullshit! There was no damn Love Generation! There was a scene, yeah, but I wasn't a part of their scene. I had my own scene back in those days, man. My own damn scene!"

Last night, among the tents and kiosks of the busy *toidu tänav* (food street), I saw the Tigress. The white-blonde hair. Those eyes. Is she the only one left who can get through to my heart? I didn't have the nerve to even approach her though. I just let her roam and vanished away.

In the corner by the pancake booth, a group of Hungarians amazes and astounds – *Hop! Hop!* – The organ grinder grinds, the wail of the fiddler, the plunk of the bass, and then that dancer who keeps slapping his thighs and leaping – *Hop! Hop!* – then some pitched group crooning. One holds a beer glass in the air as he sings, as if toasting himself. *Hop! Hoppah!* This is how it goes.

In the yard a bit later, I encounter a bunch of the Designer's friend Linnuke's amber-colored hair on a bench outside the window. Linnuke is another one of these young lady drifters who comes to sleep in the Designer's apartment. Linnuke is a bookbinder from Tallinn with fair, pretty Baltic Finnish looks and light angelic hair. She works in the archives, fixing old books. Sometimes she fixes old dolls. She is quite talented, though a little sarcastic like the rest of them.

The Designer attracts such gun-mouthed people. There's just a clump of hair on the table. It's so odd to me, just like the bra hanging from the window. Folk dishes up these kinds of surprises. Pets, the Designer's vegan sister, is training to become a hairstylist. Linnuke is one of her new clients. I was going to throw out the clumps of cut angel hair, but Linnuke protests.

They have to burn the hair in a sacrificial ceremony, says our Linnuke. "We're pagans now," she says.

Later, through a courtyard window, the same room is visible and bright, a square of yellow in the hushed darkness. The centerpiece is the ornate mirror (aside from the cat perched on the window frame). This is the fulcrum, the sun of the evening preparations. The Designer marches from the back room in a black dress and smooths it while observing her reflection.

Hair styling is happening in every corner. She runs her hands down its sides, peaks over her shoulder, bites her lip, then marches back into the room where she disappears from view. On the floor, Linnuke and the others are sipping whiskey, but soon they too will vanish behind the curtain. They parade out in black, then in white, then pose, model, seek reassurance, validation, criticism. Is my hair better up or down? Or, like this? The lipstick comes out, the rouge on the lips, an arching of the back, they turn and face each other almost in mechanical fashion, like ballet dancers in a music box.

Then the Designer emerges from behind the curtain, all dressed in white. She is stunning. A Valkyrie!

"What do you think?" she asks.

I cross myself.

"Oh," she says and touches my shoulder. "It's not easy being friends with girls, is it?"

"I think you look wonderful."

She gives me a doubtful face. Then she marches back behind the curtain. Kata replaces her before the mirror, a young woman from the West Coast with a dark bush of curly hair who is known to disappear from time to time to a cloister on Saaremaa. This mysterious visitor, Kata, keeps a small Orthodox Christian prayer book beside her bed by the window. Once, we even prayed together. It felt good when Kata said the prayers. It was one of the first times I had prayed in years and years. "Forgive us father, for we have sinned," she prayed. "Forgive us for our sins."

I couldn't even remember all of my sins.

"Well," Kata says. "I'm ready to go. I've been ready for ages."

"What are you doing back there anyway?" I call out to the Designer behind the curtain.

No answer comes. Then Linnuke answers for her. "She's sewing her dress, I think."

She really is. She is sewing her dress. Everything that night has to be perfect.

The next day. On Friday afternoon I am on desk duty at the Waldorf School. I'm very hungover, and then the Chef arrives with a beer and a box of cake to surprise me. He's like that, you know. Our Chef can't just come emptyhanded, he has to have some food with him. I can't be bothered to even look at it. I play Frank Sinatra's "Strangers in the Night" on my phone instead and he and Musi begin to dance in the foyer of the school. I take the hand of a nearby hippie woman – Väike is her name – and start to dance with her, until her bearded husband shows up and claps his hands to show me that my turn with Miss Väike is over.

I'm still not sure how the accommodation system works here though it's been explained to me so many times and I am supposedly responsible for it. Musi therefore takes control of the whole operation while the Chef and I try to talk, but I am too tired to talk anyway. There are blurry memories of last night after the girls left. I vaguely recall drinking moonshine with some people in a parking lot. People stumble in, leave, and in one room Annika Mändmaa is giving jew harp and flute lessons to some eager children. Then a man in nothing but a speedo arrives dripping, fresh from a lake swim. A Finn, apparently. The naked Finn takes a key and I doze off in the chair, vanquished. The Chef is annoyed with me. He was expecting some kind of party at the school, but I'm barely alive as it is.

"We were supposed to have fun here together," he says. "That's why I put us here on the list together! But look at you! You're so tired of life. So tired of life already!" He's right. I am tired. But I also want to go out and buy more blueberries on the food street.

Saturday morning. I bring the ladies breakfast in bed. After lounging in the morning hours on the beach with a certain Tallinn businesswoman in a bikini who laments her tan line and such, I come in with a greasy paper bag of poppyseed and cinnamon rolls and the Designer looks up from her tangles like a sleepy angel and there is peace in Linnuke's flesh as she heaves beneath the blanket. (Kata, our Orthodox Christian saint, has already gone to the woman's singing room early, with a feather in her hair). But they still can be the most awful jerk women, for the fun of it, with me.

Linnuke broods over coffee because of some man problems, and the Designer curls on the couch bemoaning her lack of suitable *noormees* (young man) at last night's dance again, despite all the preparation, primping, sewing, inspecting, *et cetera*, but she's also quiet, even kind. Curious. Then she asks me to fetch her dress and underwear from the line, which I am too happy to do.

"You are the perfect gentleman," she says.

"Don't worry, I wore gloves," I say handing over her lacy undies. I pour our Linnuke some hot coffee before she disappears into the shower but she looks down into it and frowns.

"But, you put milk in it!" she says. "Don't you know I like to drink my coffee black?"

Later that day, at the *Kultuurihoov*, or "Culture Yard," behind Sakala Keskus on Turu Street. It's a hot day. The sweat runs into your eyes, and the arena has the ambiance of a drained swimming pool. Hundreds are gathered around before the stage, on the balcony, just to see this peculiar group and its peculiar drummer, the one they call Silver, as if he was made of precious metal. He stands in the back with three tubs of water with inverted plastic containers, each of them miked. He is our blond, Finno-Ugric Jesus, with long flowing golden hair and an ever-amused smile. Somehow, he is styled as a percussionist, though you will never see him behind a drum kit. The first time I saw this Silver character play in the Ait years ago, he was playing an old bicycle tire.

Ro:toro might be the weirdest group to come out of Viljandi ever. Bagpipe? And soprano saxophone? It sounds like some kind of medieval psychedelic bar mitzvah band. At the end of the show, after the kamikaze encore, Silver hoists a bucket of water up and dumps it all over me.

"This is holy water," proclaims Silver. "Holy bagpipe water! You've now been christened by Folk!" I see the water coming. I see the water in the air and I see it splashdown all over me. Later at home my daughter just shakes her head when she sees my big wet mess. This is her father, don't forget, and he comes home soaked? "But what really happened to you?" she asks.

"Silver, the percussionist for Ro:toro, baptized me at the *Kultuurihoov*," I answer her. "I've been baptized by holy folk bagpipe water!"

Later that night, the real Saturday Night at Folk, drinking reveries come on. The rooftop of the Ait seems to accommodate excess bodies, fiddle players mostly, and many others, but some civilians come too. It's like mice coming out of a hole, there's just more and more of them. There are boastful exclamations, jokes, dances, and the Hungarians seem to be running things – *Hop! Hop!* – they take everything over. I'm in the corner drinking white wine because Mr. Aivar had to show up with a bottle and cups, of course, plus two extra bottles of red. He's like a phantom. The ghost of the Viljandi Boatman. He appears out of the clouds whenever your cup is empty with more wine.

"Would you care for some red wine?" asks Mr. Aivar. "Or, would you prefer the white?"

"I'll have the red, please." All night and into the morning, we are up here celebrating. The music is relentless. The light over the rooftops, that Islamic-looking slice of moon. The spire of St. John's Church. I am so drunk by now I don't know what to do with myself. I feel lost up here. All I can say is, "Just take everything! Take everything, my soul, my bones! Help yourselves!"

"This," the Designer grabs my chin, "is your *elu põhimõte*. The main idea of your life." Then she disappears to dance with someone else.

Sunday, the big hangover. Hot coffee and savory buns for brunch. The streets and avenues are now half-full at best. The sonorous sound of a lone fiddle on the way to the lake is the antidote to everything. A good hot bake in the sun. Last night was Tintura again. A beautiful yummy band. With electronica, *folktronica*? At night, they were up on the rooftop again, playing, jamming. Karoliina never actually stops playing. Fiddle, zither. Never. Her fingers are tireless.

The final concert takes place around 10 PM as a breeze blows in and cuts away at the heat. The lake in the distance is a silvery gash. The whole experience of Folk is so disjointed, so overwhelming. I try to jot it all down. What happened when? And to whom? And what happened next? I can't even remember it all. The light sounds of the last songs move with the breeze and for the first time all weekend, I shiver from the cold. The walls of the castle are all lit up in red. The dirty unwashed Folk faces. Somehow the festival refuses to die. Even tomorrow when the boxes of beer are put away and the stage is dismantled, one will still hear the echoes of Folk.

After the last concert, there is another last concert on Kirsimägi, and after that last concert, a small group of die-hards numbering in the low hundreds congregate around the steps of the Ait, where Ando Kiviberg himself reviews the revelers with the poise of a wise king. This is followed by a rousing king's speech from the man with the beard and cap who started it all.

"Good people of Folk," he begins. "There will only be more folk festivals! Many, many more! There will be at least 10 more years of Folk, if not double that!" He then launches into a lengthy call-and-response *regilaul*, thereafter a peculiar hide-and-seek game called *hoven toven*.

People hide themselves beneath tables and behind concession stands and old stone walls.

"Hoven," cries out Kiviberg, and people leap out into the streets again and cry back to him, "T O V E N!" Then the sound of the bagpipes again, the commanding percussion of the snare drum, keeping time. Kulno, one of the better-known folk musicians from Riffarica, and Peedu, another Viljandier in a jazz hipster beret, come marching through the crowds in army fatigues with two boys walking ahead of them, carrying fluorescent wands in their hands like swords. The crowd gasps! Then everyone salutes them. After this parade clears, they turn back to Ando and sing him a "Happy Birthday", for it's his 50th today, this last day of Folk, but he waves away his admirers.

"No, no, enough of that," Kiviberg says. "This isn't for me, it's for everyone. It's for us!"

It was for us. If we wanted more, he said, we would just have to come back next year.

THE HARVEST PARTY

"The tiger bears his claws and shows his teeth. 'Man, man, you have set me free!'"
(Tuup, British storyteller at the Harvest Party, 2019.)

In the main hall of the Ait, people are already stirring. It is 5 PM, in early October, autumn toned and rain slicked foliage outside, a faint light in the sky. There are lines of Christmas lights running here and there, decorations for this festival or party, the Harvest Party. Tonight, in the Ait, the award ceremony will take place. I have been to three of these award shows so far, and I still have no idea of what's going on.

There is voting beforehand – this I know – and there are concerts – this I also know. Each winner gets a giant wooden ladle. The "ethno ladle" or *etnokulp*. I have no idea what the significance of the ladle is, but these awards are coveted. All night long, the members of Puuluup and Black Bread Gone Mad have been tossing in their beds dreaming of giant spoons, and what they might say in their acceptance speeches. If this was happening in the US, they'd probably thank God, but since this is Estonia, they'll probably just say "thanks" and leave it at that.

Inside the Ait, in the Great Hall or *Suur Saal*, Tubli the drummer from Trad.Attack! is seated by his kit in the dark, his laptop glowing beside him. Tubli is silent while the other sound checks go on. He's dressed in a suit – Tubli takes this drumming business very seriously – and he sits in his chair like he's always here, like some kind of wind-up toy, where you just slip in a 2€ coin and he'll drum away for 15 minutes. He bangs on the cymbals a few times just to show he's ready to go.

I still feel like a bit of an outsider at the Ait. I am not yet included within the folkie social network, although I sense my time as an apprentice may be coming to an end, and soon they will let me in. One day Lee, one of the violinists from Black Bread Gone Mad, even said "Hello" to me in the store. Kulno also waves to me, and even Jalmar himself greets me as a friend. Maybe, there's a special ceremony involved. Maybe, I too will be given a giant wooden spoon?

At the Harvest Party, all my old friends arrive. The Designer wears a white dress, and Linnuke has some kind of majestic black one draped around her, with silver sewn into the fabric. She looks like a chocolate pastry. I end up dancing with neither of them though.

Instead, I twirl around with a girl in a revealing polka-dot dress. I specifically decide to dance with her because Paavo the writer has been buying me beers all night. Every time I turn around, Paavo is there with another one of his "gifts" and that satanic smile of his saying, "Drink up."

"It will make you a better writer," he says. "Drink like me and you'll write 10 novels!"

Paavo has been trying to co-opt me into the writer's world of drink for months. He's even made me the interviewer for the upcoming launch of his new book, *Kongo Tango*. The Estonian Writers' Union awarded this latest book first prize. He tells everyone about this great victory. "Did I mention I got first prize for *Kongo Tango*?" says Paavo, handing me another beer.

I keep my eyes focused on the dots on the girl's dress. I've discovered that I will not get sick as we dance together. When my eyes stay trained on the polka-dots, it is as if I'm standing still, rather than being whirled around to the sounds of Lee's intense violin. If I just keep looking at her dress, then I won't throw up.

The musical duo Puuluup are next up on the stage, and they are singing their hit single "*Lambale Joo*." Their music is terrific fun. It's as if Veisson and Ramo mixed reggae with Alpine yodeling, a bit of new wave, and then add their own personal weirdness. Their music speaks to the unknowable depth of the Estonian soul, you see. Everyone loves Puuluup. They are the victors of the Harvest Party and win almost every *etnokulp*.

Only Black Bread puts up any kind of fight. They don't know how to savor victory though. This is not like when those Formula One race drivers win a rally and ladies come out in bikinis and dump bottles of champagne all over them. Veisson and Ramo are stiff, aloof, and reserved. "Well, uh, yeah ... thanks. *Aitäh*." This is all they say. About 3,000 people voted this year, 2,500 more than last year. (Or, I think, maybe our friend Silver the drummer voted 2,500 times this year? And if he did, who knew he was such a Puuluup fan?)

Ramo with his wisps of blond-white hair and black jacket looks like an old preacher from the country. Veisson with his beard, glasses, and serious demeanor reminds me of a Jewish rabbi. Whoever they are, Puuluup are certainly men of god. There is an austere, ecclesiastical mood to their performance. They sing songs about giving the sheep something to drink, or about lighting their snow on fire (*"Süütu Mu Lumi"*) and, especially, about their birch trees. This last number is my favorite. *"Kus on minu kasekesed? Kus on minu kasekesed?"* ("Where are my little birches? Where are my little birches?") they ask. *"Metsas on. Metsas on."* ("In the forest. In the forest.")

This is what I listen to as the girl with the polka-dot dress swirls around me. Because of the lighting, sometimes the dots are black and other times they are white. After the concert, we are all seated upstairs (where I can see the dots are white, not black) at a round table with Veisson. He makes little wry jokes that I cannot understand and everyone laughs at his jokes. It must be nice, Veisson, it must be nice to be a musical god and have more spoons than one knows what to do with! All the women laugh at Veisson's jokes and I leer at him.

I've become an ornery, jealous drunk, and the girl in the polka-dot dress wants nothing to do with me. "Why do you keep staring at my dress?" she asks, "It's so creepy!"

In the corner, the Designer and a handsome young musician are dancing. She looks so happy dancing with him and it makes me somehow sad to see their happiness. Then gentlemanly Veisson takes our beautiful Linnuke by the hand and escorts her to dance along too. I turn to speak to the girl in the polka-dot dress, but she's already gone.

There's just no one for me here tonight. There's no one I can count on. All I can see is the Designer with her back turned to me. She has her back to me, and she is enjoying her dance with the musician. I tell myself I am not jealous, but I feel now that something has changed. It is as if she took me under her wing for a while, nurtured me, but now, it's time for me to move on. And so, as she dances around the room with the musician, and Linnuke with her dear Mr. Veisson, I grab my things and slip out the door. They never inquire after me either. I'm already heading downstairs.

The real treat of the concert is the Ruhnu Room, which is arranged in the *väike saal* (small hall). This is where Lee, Karoliina, and Sänni perform folk songs on their fiddles for the crowds. The hall is standing-room-only by the time they begin, the air hot and full of positive energy.

I feel rather desperate watching the ladies play their instruments. I would like to play too. I would like to rejoin the musical world and leave this writerly world behind sometimes. I can see how the music enriches their souls and bodies and makes them so beautiful. I've set myself up in the front row to get as close at them as I can. To watch everything unfold. My journal is open, but then I put it away.

Lines start to form, lines of dancers. These are the amazing line dances that characterize almost all events at the Ait. Lines of couples going over and under, and in between. Spinning, spinning. In the breaks, Kairi Leivo, the raven-haired, most mutinous and unruly member of the folk ensemble Naised Köögis, tells bawdy stories about time spent on Ruhnu Island, that tiny speck of land in the Gulf of Riga that was once home to Coastal Swedes. Ruhnu has recently become something of a cultural spring or *allikas* for this group of folk performers. Especially for Karoliina, who leads musical pilgrimages to the remote island where time stands still.

There's a bar in the corner of the Ruhnu Room, of course, where they offer different alcoholic beverages, and so, I am there in an instant to drown my sorrows. So, I have lost the Designer, Linnuke, and also the polka-dot dress girl. But there is a dark lager called *Ruhnu Karu* (Ruhnu Bear) and it has a picture of a bear on it. There is also a lighter lager called *Ruhnu Hüljes* (Ruhnu Seal). These are my new best friends. To lift my spirits even higher, Mr. Aivar is at the bar in a tan jacket, of course, conversing with the bartenders. There is a strange link between me, Mr. Aivar, and alcohol, I must acknowledge, but I am not sure what it is. He just happens to appear whenever I am down on my luck with a bottle or two. And if not him, then Merit the Lioness, with chilled bottles of fine wines. These people. They are the ruin and redemption of me. That first night back at Fellin seems long ago, but they are still here. They are part of the Viljandi dream.

"Give me two of the seal!" I say and pull out my wallet, but Aivar has already paid for it. "It's on me," he says in his good-humored way. No worries." The seal, I say, is my spirit animal.

"But why a seal?" Mr. Aivar responds. "I personally would choose a bear."

"Naturally, you would for bears represent strength, authority. Seals symbolize creativity!"

"Yes, of course," he says with his marvelous grin. This is what we talk about in Viljandi.

There is a lonely man at the bar, sipping on a cold bottle of Ruhnu Fox. This lonely man is one of the better-known folk musicians. And he is lonely, I learn, because his wife has just left him.

"But why would she leave you?" I ask. "You're one of the best players in the land!"

"Tell her that!"

"It is a goddamn travesty I tell you!"

"Tell her!"

"Tragic!"

"It is what it is."

His sadness, his emotionality is striking. It is so rare that I ever see an Estonian express any amount of emotion. They are always so cool, so calm. I just can't help but feel for this man.

I used to be him.

"You know, there is nothing you could have done about it anyway," I tell the musician. "There is no avoidance in these kinds of things in life. You can't blame yourself for anything."

"That's exactly what I've been doing. Blaming myself!"

"Don't even bother. Just go with the flow. Just move forward."

The musician seems a bit relieved. He still looks lonely though. The sad musician nods, then disappears into the crowds, his bottle of Ruhnu Fox beer dangling limply from one of his hands. I watch him sadly too. I used to be just a ghost of a man. But something else has breathed new life into me now. Someone comes by, takes my hand and we rejoin the snaking line dance.

In the corner, a trio of ladies, on their violins, play a tune called "*Kom Vännen*". In the Swedish language this means "Come, My Friend *(Tule, Sōber)*".

A BRILLIANT NEW START

"Something good will come out of all things yet – And it will be golden and eternal just like that – There's no need to say another word."
(Jack Kerouac (1922–1969), Big Sur, 1962.)

One morning while drinking coffee with the intrepid Mr. Aivar, freshly returned from a trip aboard the ship *Bellings-hausen* to Antarctica, we discuss our backup plans. Should we be driven from Viljandi, by war, pandemic, or some other calamity, our only solution will be to recreate Viljandi elsewhere, perhaps at a warming South Pole. There, we shall establish "New Viljandi," set up a new Green House Cafe, a new Fellin, a new Ugala. Everything will be like the Old Viljandi, just new. Instead of the "Paalalinn" ("Paala Town") district we shall have the "Ennulinn" ("Enn's Town") district. Instead of "Peetrimõisa" ("Peter's Manor") we'll have "Aivarimõisa" ("Aivar's Manor"). Instead of "Männimäe" ("Pine Hill"), we'll have "Pinguiinimäe" ("Penguin Hill").

All the same, but just a bit different.

During the day, we will drink from our hot cups and toss breadcrumbs to the penguins. I am sure the Chef will come and find work there at one of the new restaurants opening up in New Viljandi. Knowing the strange supernatural pull of the town, it won't be long before the Designer shows up on her bike, or Simon the Engineer is in the corner complaining about the weather. I think that Jaak will be there talking of Jean-Paul Sartre, Pepi the Argentinian and Tubli will be playing table tennis. We all belong to Viljandi, or rather Viljandi is us. We are the town and the town is us.

Nii on. So it is.

Mr. Aivar has agreed to this plan in principle.

"Oh, my dear friend," he says. "You really are in such a splendid mood today."

"Let's hope it doesn't come to that," I tell him, my cup of hot macchiato swishing around. "But if it does come to that, if we do someday need to leave this blessed soil, we know what to do. Just think of it. We could all start over again in Antarctica. It would be a brilliant new start!"

Mr. Aivar isn't sure what to make of me. He's actually a man of few words. When I asked him, what Antarctica was like, he told me that it was "*päris külm*," rather cold. That's all he said. Still, we'll need him for our new community. His friend, the adventurer Pruuli, can sail the ship *Bellingshausen* back and forth with supplies. The deck will be loaded with sacks of black beans.

"New Viljandi." It sounds like the title of a future novel, I think. What a setting! Such characters! Can you imagine the drama? The intrigues? I can't tell anyone else about it. Not yet.

I haven't heard a word from our wayward friend the Chef these days. I assume he's been busy with work at the hotel where everyone salutes this long-haired Swede as their boss and personal savior. Yet one day, there's a faint knock at my door. I don't answer, but then comes another rap. The door creaks open and I see that face of his peering through the crack.

"You actually knocked two times," I say. "I'm impressed."

"Do you mind if I come in?"

"Make yourself at home."

"We need to talk," he says, entering. "But first, we also need to have some coffee."

The new moka espresso maker I recently bought is set to boil – I can't bear to tell him that I left the small one he loaned me months ago on the stove one morning while I was writing and all the plastic melted. I don't think he remembers. He doesn't remember because he works too much.

"Do you have any cream?" he asks and when I give him some, he takes a seat. Who is this tired shell of a man? He used to be full of *sisu* and derring-do. Now he has full-blown burnout. Some of the hair on the sides of his head looks a little lighter. Is he going gray? Or is it the lighting?

"Well, that's it," he says, staring at his feet. "It's over."

"What's over?"

"The whole thing. We had a meeting before and we decided. It's over."

"What are you talking about?"

"I've been on the phone with Erik in Sweden all day talking about it."

Bit by bit, the truth trickles out. The Chef's days at Ormisson have come to an end. This crowning achievement of his illustrious career as a head chef has ended in subterfuge and gloom. It's unclear at this moment what procedure for this departure will be employed, but he is either fired or he has resigned. Something is not right about the affair. But the final decision is that his position is lost. So that's it. A chapter in the Chef's saga is over. Yet a new one will soon begin.

"Someday," he says, "I am going to write a book about this goddamn life. All of it!" He groans and rubs at his temples with his hands. He looks up and pours himself another strong *fika*. "God, look at this apartment," he says. "You should get another one. Or clean this one."

"Why?"

"Why? Just look at it."

"Thanks a lot."

"I'm serious. Get a better place. Then maybe you can have something of a personal life."

"A personal life?"

"Yes, some people have these things called personal lives. They have partners. They go out to dinner, or to the theater, or to the movies, and they do things together. They go on trips."

"That's not what this Viljandi life is about for me."

"I can see that."

He looks around the room again, sniffs at his coffee. "I did hear from my friend in Oslo. He's working out on an oil rig now."

"The one with the blowup doll?"

"You have a good memory. He says I can get a job in his old hotel, if I want. It's good money. The Norwegians do pay well. More money than I'll ever see in this town, that's for sure."

"That's something to consider."

"Yes. But one thing is certain. This part of my life is done. I have to start again."

"But that's good. Rebirth is good. Life is about rebirth."

"If you say so." It's a somber moment for our Chef. His life is a string of military defeats. I feel our noble Swede will pull through though. He's 36. I was 36 when this Viljandi life started.

I'm sworn to secrecy about the Chef's situation, but at the cafe, no one is interested anyway. As soon as I enter the next morning, Enn walks over to me and says in a hushed tone, "Kaari's father Rein passed away last night. Funeral plans underway. Would be nice if you could come."

Old Rein. You would see him in the yard of the cafe over the past few summers, sitting in the corner with his hat and cane, wiping sweat from his brow. I'd recently seen him in the shop. He was pushing a cart and leaning on it to hold himself up.

Rein once held some high rank in the Soviet army, but I could never recall what it was. I think he was a captain, but I always saluted him as a general. "My general! *Mu kindral!*" I said to him in the shop. Rein had laughed and said, "You know, people always ask me, '*Rein, kuidas käsi käib?* How is your hand doing? I always tell them my hand is fine, *käsi käib hästi*, but these legs aren't so fine. *Jalad enam ei käi.*"

Two days later he was gone.

The funeral is at St. Paul's Church on the hill. It has a beautiful wood interior with fine chandeliers. Enn is there in front with his hat in his gnarled, workman's hands. "The poor son of a bitch," he says. Rein is gone, but Enn is still moving on. He's just a few years younger than Rein, but he seems to be eons younger. Rein seemed to have lived his life. Enn will need a few more decades. Maybe he will become one of these supercentenarians and live to the age of 110. One can only hope. He'll still be roasting coffee, I'm sure, and maybe I will marry some younger girl and start running things. Even if we have to relocate the whole operation to the South Pole.

Enn asks me if I will be a pallbearer and help out at the Forest Cemetery or *Metsakalmistu.*

"We just don't have enough strong young men. Do you think you can do it?"

"Of course, I will."

"I'll give you all the macchiatos you want. *Tume röst!* Anything you need!"

"No, no, no. We're like family now, Enn. Family. It would be an honor."

When the church service has ended, I grip the handles and help move the coffin into the hearse. It's a grim, wet funeral parade out at the Forest Cemetery. This is the newer cemetery out past Uueveski that is full of fog and pines. Into this panorama are sketched a few dark figures.

We lower the coffin into the ground, cover it with pine branches, and then we take turns tossing handfuls of dirt into Rein's grave. The priest says a few words, and then it's time for us to go to work with the shovels. We work to fill the grave in. Enn and Kaari are there with me and a few other relatives. We finish it off, and then it's back to the town, and the warmth of the cafe.

There is mud all over my pants from the grave digging, and my hands are still cold from the Forest Cemetery, but I feel warm inside. I feel warm and youthful and hopeful, because that very morning I had seen a familiar young woman in a Nepali shirt on Kauba Street. She had very beautiful eyes, freckles, and soft tufts of golden hair. When she passed me, we exchanged a greeting. I told her I was going to a funeral. She told me she was going to Sōbralt Sōbrale. We made no plans to meet, but I knew that in this town it was inevitable that our paths would cross.

On the last day of the last month of the last year of the decade, I awake at the crack of sunlight, and set the moka espresso maker to boil, and get a good fire going. Then, ever so carefully, after sitting down at my table, I start to write. Just a taste of coffee and the words start to flow. I love that feeling, that feeling of the flow when the words come.

After I have had my fill of morning writing, I decide to take a walk to enjoy the sunshine on the facades of the pretty Old Town. I collect my things into my canvas writing bag – my journal, a few pens – and I head outside.

It's at the corner of Posti and Koidu Streets when I see her again.

She really does look like a tiger. She has light freckles and hair of gold and curious eyes. Her coat is covered with stripes. There is a bit of an up-and-down rhythm when she walks, as if she is headed somewhere of great importance, yet I already know her too well. She has no idea of where she is going. This person is not a slow-moving ship. This is a person who pounces. I know she left the country. I know she left the country and has had all kinds of adventures since.

It is this jungle energy, her impulsiveness, that always captivates me. My soul swoons to see her, standing just like that on the corner of Koidu and Posti streets, in the light of this late December day. I wave cautiously as I approach her and she waves back. We approach each other carefully, sizing the other up. She smiles at me, a brilliant sun of a smile. She really is a true friend.

"*Head vana aasta lõppu,*" I say.

"The same to you."

"A happy ending to the old year, and a happy new year too."

"Yes, it's been a year now, hasn't it?" she squints. "Exactly one year."

It has been a year since I saw her at the end of Monk Street in the snow. She had wished me a 'Happy New Year', and I'd promised to return her the favor. My time has now come to do it.

"I have been waiting all this time to fulfill my duty. So that you shall have good luck. Now my task has been fulfilled."

"But that is all you wanted then? To fulfill your task?"

"That, and to love you now and then. If I may?"

Something always compels me to push things in that direction with her. Surely, I haven't imagined a future for us, where we elope and move into one of the shining mansions of Peetrimõisa where a second brood of children bounces happily on some backyard trampoline.

Surely, I haven't conjured the day when her parents, who are my age, arrive for coffee and reflect on the good old days under Comrade Gorbachev. Surely, such outlandish ideas have never crossed my mind. Yet there is love at the root of this whole equation, and it needs to be sorted out. Such things are too crucial to let them fade into the winter sun on the last day of the year.

"Hmm," she weighs the proposition. "I do understand you, but often we want to put our feelings in a box. We think that if we love someone, it should manifest as something more."

"But I don't want anything more. Only the opportunity to love you sometimes."

"Well then love away. You're always welcome to love me. Love me as much as you can."

"And to write about you too sometimes, because you inspire me to write."

"Then write away. Write until your heart is contented. I am actually honored to inspire you."

"You are honored?"

I stop and eye her like a Spanish conquistador having stumbled upon a lost city of gold. Honored? It couldn't be true. All this time, I have been searching for a new muse. Someone who will allow me to love them with words. Now there is someone who will even be *honored?*

"Are you sure?"

"Yes," she nods. "Why wouldn't I be?"

I sigh very audibly, and she shoots me a concerned look, but I let it go. How do you tell someone who is just starting out in the world all the things you've been through? Dark things? Brutal things? I just can't tell her about it. Not yet. Hopefully never. I want to forget it all too.

We walk a bit side by side. Through the trees I can see the smoke from the chimneys and the friendly dome of the Mäe Street church, and its golden glinting cross above it. I look at the golden cross and for the first time since I moved to Viljandi I no longer feel fear or concern.

I look at the sun and love its golden color. This town has actually been so good to me, you know. This town has given me many brilliant ideas and experiences. The temperature has dropped, and there are chunks of cracked ice on the side-walks. It feels good to walk on the crunchy mirrors beside the Tigress in silence and I only want more of her presence. If I let the feelings warm me, I can write dozens of novels! Her wood can warm my furnaces for all of golden eternity.

"So where are you going now?" I ask her as we walk along.

"I'm going to a cafe."

"But which one?"

"The best one, of course."

"Oh," I say. "Then maybe I will come and join you."

It seems like a happy ending. Two characters meet on a sun-kissed, cold December day. The last day of the year. A new year that brings with it promises of new beginnings, of new life.

A whole new decade awaits them both, just a few hours away. What could possibly go wrong?

EVERYONE YOU EVER LOVED

"Is it all a dream or real? We still don't understand."
(Kristiina Ehin, "A Changed World," March 2020.)

Two weeks into quarantine, a deep frost settles into Viljandi and with the light snow and ice, a hush or calm comes over the entirety of the town. From the tip of Kirsimägi one can look along the valley around the lake and see all of the gold lights on the ground twinkling like stars in the sky. After a long solemn stroll through deserted streets, I arrive home, take off my shirt, pants, and thermal underwear, and climb into bed.

I stare out the window for a while at the Old Water Tower and watch the wisps of clouds passing behind its rooftop. Viljandi. No matter the startled shape of the world, it will always be a friend through it all. I recall how I came here years ago. I remember my birthday night, and all about that strange girl on the beach, the one I called Miss Cloud. Only once in a while do I still hear from her. So much has happened since then, and so much has changed inside of me. Yet now and then I still remember her. Sometimes she sends me a photo of a glacier or a rainbow. That's all. I still feel she is out there.

I watch the Old Water Tower.

This is how I drift off to sleep.

At about 2 AM, I seem to awaken with a start. I toss and turn and at last decide it's no use, so I pull on my pants and sweater, and lace up my winter boots and go out for a walk.

I come down Mäe Street past the old Orthodox church, peer in its windows, and then around into Liiva Street, enjoying the frost on the bushes, trees, and fences, and the crunch of one's feet on the snow. All of Viljandi is asleep at this time. There are no other sounds, no other voices. By the lake, there is no one. All is silent but the creak of the boats in the water. Only the Old Boathouse is lit up, revealing its wooden contours.

In the summer, I came down here once with the Designer. There had been a pop-up cafe serving pea soup and there was a boating competition on that day. We were good friends on that summer day, and there was a good feeling between us. Now this place is so desolate and almost abandoned. The lights from the many villas on the hill glow like ghosts. I start to feel I should go home then, standing next to all that icy water. How many stories go just like this: "Daddy went out for a walk at night, and he didn't come home." I have a mug of hot tea with me and I try to finish drinking it beside the lake. But it's so cold that the tea is frozen. I set the mug down beside the Old Boathouse.

I wait there, watching.

While at the dock by the lake, I notice a shadowy form moving through the mists. Yet I'm not afraid to see it. When things happen that we do not understand, we do not always feel fear.

It's a flat boat, rowed by an old man dressed in black. Behind him stands a dark shape. At first, I take it to be a sack of potatoes or maybe coffee beans from Enn's cafe. But then the form stands and moves slowly towards me. The shape is dressed in a cloak. It steps from the boat onto the dock and strides toward me. When the shape pulls back its black hood, I can see who it is.

"Good evening, *Härra* Petrone!"

"Miss Cloud?"

"One and the same."

"Oh," part of me melted away. "Oh, how I have missed your beautiful fat Finnish face."

"You think my face is fat?"

"As beautiful and as fat as a baby seal's."

"You sure are strange, Petrone. I guess I will have to take it as a compliment."

"But why are you here? Why did you come back?"

"We've been sent to take you to the other side of the lake."

"*We?*" I glance over her shoulder, and notice there are two other shapes in dark robes. The first steps forward and removes her hood so that I can see the numbers of the year painted in silver on her cheek and her golden curls framing those luminous enchanting tiger eyes.

"But you're here too?"

"*Njahh*," she said.

"What do you mean? *Njahh*?"

"Yes and no. *Nii ja naa.*"

Beside her I can see the third woman pull back her hood. It's the Designer, of course! She winks at me a few times and I notice a smaller shape by her feet that struts toward me on all fours and purrs. It's her favorite black cat, the stray she once found on Posti Street in Viljandi. A mysterious woman in a black cloak with a black cat. She had been a witch all along. I knew it.

"And you even brought your cat," I remark to the Designer.

"Of course," she says, scooping him in her arms. "He's always with me."

"All three of you then," I say. "Like those maidens in Arthurian legend, come to heal me. Is that why you are all here? To heal me?"

"But you don't need to be healed anymore," says Miss Cloud.

"Why not?"

"Because you're already healed."

"What do you mean?"

"You have learned to love again."

"I have?" My eyes moisten in the cold wind.

"Crying again?" says the Designer. "But there's no need to cry anymore."

"It's just the wind."

"Of course, it is."

"So, what happens now?" I ask.

"Time to celebrate," says Miss Cloud. "There's another cafe on the other side of the lake. All of our friends are there already, waiting for us."

"Is the Chef there?"

"Yes, that Swedish rascal is there waiting."

"And Musi?

"She is waiting, and Linnuke is waiting there too, with Kata. Enn and Kaari are waiting."

"What about Heldi? And Jõeste?"

"Yes! Yes! And Kangilaski, and Simon the Engineer too."

"But Aivar and Merit?"

"They are there too, Petrone, and so is Emma. They brought loads of wine."

"But Silver?"

"Silver is there too, with all of his musical contraptions. And Naised Köögis are there. Remo and Veisson from Puuluup. Everyone you have ever loved. They are all there."

"Even Jalmar, Sandra, and Tubli?"

"All of Trad.Attack! And Zetod too."

"But I can't go just yet. I have to go to the Green House. I have to finish my book!"

"You'll have all the time you need to finish your books on the other side of the lake. All the macchiatos you'll ever need. Just take my hand, *Härra* Petrone. Take my hand and come."

"Come?"

"Come, come," says Miss Cloud. "You can always come with me."

I take Miss Cloud's hand and step onto the boat. Her hand is supple, soft, and warm. And it soothes me to hold it. She nods once to the boatman, who begins to stir at the icy waters with his oar, propelling us farther from the shore. "Don't worry," the Tigress whispers in my ear, taking my other hand fully in hers, "We'll blow a little sunshine into that frosty old heart of yours."

Soon the lights from the villas on the hill are no longer visible through the mist.

This is how we vanish together into the clouds.

MORE BY THIS AUTHOR

„MY ESTONIA. PASSPORT FORGERY, MEAT JELLY EEATERS AND OTHER STORIES"

Some people have told me this book is romantic and maybe it is: a young lost American falls in love with an intriguing Estonian journalist and embarks on a journey that restores his faith in himself and the world. I agree. It is romantic. But it was never easy. A foreigner arrives in the middle of a dark winter and must survive in Estonia, the least fortunate Scandinavian country, a land where people eat blood sausage and jellied meat, drink warm bread, and are always on time; a place where every family is haunted by the past and is struggling to catch up to the present.

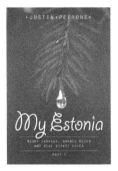

„MY ESTONIA 2. BERRY JUNKIES, NORDIC ELVES, AND REAL ESTATE FEVER"

The year was 2003. While Estonia pondered its fate as a new member of the glittering West, I wrestled with my own fate as a husband and father to be, at the age of 23. I had been drawn to northern Europe by its gem-like allure but now had to deal with the permanence of my decisions. I was being pulled apart, tugged back and forth between this land of forest people who were hard to befriend and the needs of my own big Italian-American family. As the days grew crushingly short and the polar night set in, a tense debate between destiny and free will stormed within me.

„MY ESTONIA 3. WHAT HAPPENED?"

This is the story of a man looking for his way. New York did not satisfy his soul, so he moved to Estonia, with his crazy wife, a kid, and six suitcases. Within 24 hours he found a home and had to learn how to make a fire. It did not satisfy his soul for long. Soon he had a house with four furnaces, and was making fires around the clock.

His crazy Estonian wife started a publishing house that turned out well. Too well. He decided to become an academic. It did not satisfy him for long, but at least he met a real elf who inspired him. Then he decided to dabble in diplomacy. It did not feel right either.

And he got depressed. There were too many drunks and neo-Nazis in this country, not to mention all the mice, lice, and ice. Writing books – bestsellers! – about those problems seemed to satisfy his soul. He thought he had found his niche, as a writer in a small town teeming with cafes and characters.

Then, overnight, it all collapsed.

„SKETCHES OF ESTONIA"

This book is a collection of short stories about this intriguing northern land and its engaging characters: world travelers, nudists, geneticists, writers, politicians, hitchhikers, fishermen, drunks, folk musicians, naturalists, builders, poets, clowns, blacksmiths, and tropicalists.

Photos: Justin Petrone and his friends

A glimpse of another euphoric Viljandi Folk Music Festival
at the Castle Ruins.

Kõrgemäe Street reminds one of the high hills
and colorful mansions of San Francisco.

Surreal street decorations during the Hanseatic Days Festival.
I snapped this photo while walking home at 5 AM
after DJing a set at the Airplane Factory.

People leave lost items on window sills in the Old Town.
Here, a lost teddy bear patiently awaits the return of his owner.

A street picnic in September to celebrate the birthday of Viljandi,
with the Old Water Tower in the distance.

My troublemaker friend, the Swedish Chef. Wherever there is danger, good food, and good company, he will be there.

A wooden maze for children during the annual Viljandi Folk Music Festival, a scene of total anarchy and fun for all.

A happy youth enjoys a meal at Fellin, one of the more renowned bistros in town, and a great place to write and observe people.

My dear friends Heldi and Jõeste, founding members of the cafe club at the Green House Cafe.

My friend Pets cooks up something delicious
(and completely vegan) in the courtyard of Romaan.

Viljandi Lake frozen over in midwinter. When the ski trails
are open, you can ski from one side of the lake to the other.

Jalmar Vabarna of Zetod rides the hands of his devotees at the Viljandi Folk Music Festival. Jalmar is one of the peculiar Seto types from the southeast. I don't think I'll ever figure him out.

Festival organizer and cultural instigator Ando Kiviberg and friends serenade the audience. In person, Ando is often polite and self-effacing, but at Folk he roars like a lion.

Viljandi youth enjoy a skating competition outside Romaan on Koidu Street. These kinds of street festivals are common and give people the feeling that the town belongs to them.

Enn at the controls. Most days he is in the back of the Green House Cafe roasting beans.

Here I am on my way to write somewhere.
I really took it to heart that if I was ever going to improve as a writer,
I was going to have to work on it every single day.

A boy from the Waldorf School lowers a basket of waffles
during a festival. Put your money in the basket and he'll pull it up,
fill your order, and lower a hot waffle to you.

A spring day in the yard of the Green House Cafe.

And a cozy autumn day inside, where locals swap stories.

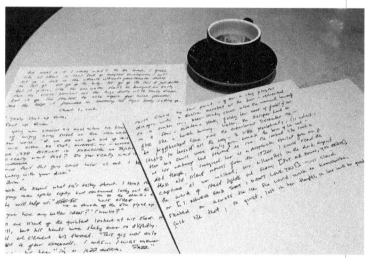

I got so tired of writing on a computer that I opted to start
writing by hand. It felt like a more natural way to compose.

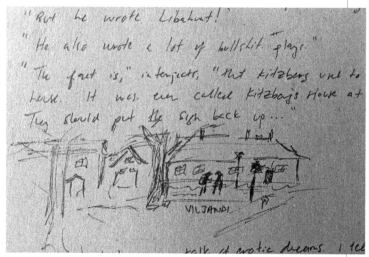

And on some days I also sketched what
I saw as I gazed out the window.

Whenever you are lonely in town,
some loving presence will make itself known.
In this case, a brick that says Kalli, „Hug".

At my „desk" working on something.
Most days, nothing special came out,
but on some days, inspiration struck.

The toilet at Romaan, where portraits of visitors, like Social Democrat Jevgeni Ossinovski, hang proudly on the walls. But how do you get your official Romaan toilet portrait? Simple. Stand in the toilet, have someone photograph you, frame it, and hang it on the wall. Done!

Here I am with my cafe pal, Emma, who believes in me and always pushes me to write better.

A clothesline somewhere on Lutsu Street
in the Old Town, giving another glimpse
of Viljandi's famed bohemian shanty life.

A view of the yard at the new cafe at Ave Nahkur's gallery on
Tartu Street. A very welcome addition to Viljandi's cafe scene.

A new woman moved in down the street and put these apples
out for passersby. She would also sit in the doorway of her
home in the mornings and drink coffee. It really felt like Italy.

The trails behind the Castle Ruins, a place to go for solitary walks,
and also full of lilacs in spring. I call them the California Hills.

CPSIA information can be obtained
at www.ICGtesting.com
Printed in the USA
BVHW051004180821
614615BV00015B/1093